Building Writing Skills

Level 2

Narrative, Argumentative/Persuasive, Informative/Explanatory Writing

Building Writing Skills series is available in print or eBook form.
- Level 1 • Level 2
- Essential Tips & Techniques

Written by
Noreen Conte

Edited by
Patricia Gray

Graphic Design by
Scott Slyter

© 2017
THE CRITICAL THINKING CO.™
www.CriticalThinking.com
Phone: 800-458-4849 • Fax: 541-756-1758
1991 Sherman Ave., Suite 200 • North Bend • OR 97459
ISBN 978-1-60144-888-0

Table of Contents

Introduction

"The most important thing is to read as much as you can, like I did. It will give you an understanding of what makes good writing and it will enlarge your vocabulary."
- J.K. Rowling

"If you want to be a writer, you must do two things above all others: read a lot and write a lot."
- Stephen King

"There is nothing to writing. All you do is sit down at a typewriter and bleed."
- Ernest Hemingway

Most people who have attempted to write papers, short stories, college applications, books, newspaper articles, letters, and even notes on greeting cards can identify with Ernest Hemingway's words. The goal of this book is to equip sixth and seventh graders with the tools they need to help them with the writing process.

Using the writing process as shown on page iv, three types of writing will be addressed: narrative writing, argumentative/persuasive writing, and informative/explanatory writing. Lessons and activities will be presented with examples and explanations to aid teachers and parents who are guiding young writers. Rubrics are provided to help evaluate the writing.

"The secret of getting ahead is getting started. The secret of getting started is breaking your complex, overwhelming tasks into small manageable tasks and then starting on the first one."
- Mark Twain

The 5-Step Writing Process on page iv will be used to separate the big task of writing into smaller tasks that are manageable.

About The Author

Noreen Conte taught reading, writing, language arts, and spelling for more than thirty years. Through the years, she gathered ideas to help students become better writers. Conte's goal in this series is to equip students with the tools they need to help them with the writing process. The Five-Step Writing Process is used to separate the big task of writing into smaller tasks that are manageable.

As a teacher, Conte enjoyed creating lesson plans and activities to motivate and challenge students. She is happy she found another way to do this though her writing. Her other books published by The Critical Thinking Co.™ are *Language Smarts E™*, *Jumbles: Prefixes, Suffixes, and Compound Words*, and *Building Writing Skills*.

Types of Writing

Narrative Writing

A true event or an imagined story.

Pages 1-47

Argumentative/ Persuasive Writing

Explains what the author or someone else believes or claims about something. It tries to convince readers to agree with the claim by providing evidence that supports the claim.

Pages 48-72

Informative/ Explanatory Writing

Gives readers information/facts about a topic. The author must research the topic using sources such as books, articles, and the Internet. The author may use illustrations and diagrams to help the reader understand the topic or just to add interest.

Pages 73-99

Personal Narrative

A personal narrative is a true story about an event or experience of the author.

Pages 1-22

Story Narrative

A story narrative is a story imagined by the author.

Pages 23-47

The 5-Step Writing Process

1. Prewriting

Brainstorm ideas for a topic.
Plan your writing: beginning, middle, and end.

2. First Draft

Use your planning to organize events in sequence.
Introductory sentence should capture the reader's interest.
Provide a conclusion.

3. Revising

Reread your writing.
Make sure your writing is presented in an organized way.
Ask a friend or family member to read your writing and give feedback.

4. Editing

Check for errors in capitalization, punctuation, spelling, word usage, and sentence structure.

5. Publishing

Share your writing. Read it aloud in class. Send copies to friends and relatives.

Personal Narrative

A **personal narrative** is a true story about an event or experience of the writer. Most personal narratives are told in the first person because the author is writing about himself or herself or a group that includes him or her.

Example: Today was the big math test. I had studied all week, and I was ready. Still, I was a little nervous, but once I started, I was fine. My teacher had asked us to get some books out to read in case we finished early. The test was easy for me, and I finished early. So, I got to read my favorite book!

5-Step Writing Process

1. **Prewriting - Time to Think**

2. **First Draft - Time to Write**

3. **Revising - Time to Improve Your Writing**

4. **Editing - Time to Make Corrections**

5. **Publishing - Time to Share**

Personal Narrative Writing Process

Use these steps to write a personal narrative.

1. Prewriting - Time to Think
- Decide on a topic to write about.
- Brainstorm—discuss your topic with others.
  - Ask: What? Who? When? Where? Why?
- Consider who will read your writing.
- Gather information about your topic.
- Organize the information—make a plan.
  - Beginning (Introduction)
  - Middle
  - End (Conclusion)

2. First Draft - Time to Write
- Use complete sentences and paragraphs to organize your information.
- Have others read it and offer suggestions.

3. Revising - Time to Improve Your Writing
- Read what you have written and make changes if needed, keeping in mind what others suggested.
  - Add descriptive words.
  - Add more detail.

4. Editing - Time to Make Corrections
- Make sure you use complete sentences, correct spelling, punctuation, and capitalization.

5. Publishing - Time to Share
- Read it aloud in class.
- Send copies to friends or relatives.

1. Prewriting → Brainstorming

A **personal narrative** is a true story about an event or experience of the writer. Most personal narratives are told in the first person because the author is writing about himself or herself or a group that includes him or her.

First Person Pronouns

I, we, me, us, mine, our, ours

 Alphonso was given a writing prompt for a personal narrative: Think of an experience you will never forget. Write a true story about this experience.

Alphonso brainstormed and wrote down ideas that he had for his personal narrative. Then he chose one topic.

What will the topic be for my personal narrative?		
breaking leg	changing schools	hurricane
surprise party	Baseball Hall of Fame	winning spelling bee
school play	snowstorm	beach
football game	Niagara Falls	first puppy

Alphonso brainstormed about visiting Niagara Falls to get some ideas on paper before organizing them in the planning step of the writing process.

Niagara Falls		
summer vacation	Niagara River	*Maid of the Mist*
visiting family in N.Y.	beautiful view	rain poncho
Niagara Falls	elevator to boats	so much water
gigantic waterfall	crashing water	got wet
Lake Erie, Lake Ontario	foam and mist	kind of scary

1. Prewriting → Planning

Planning is the process of organizing thoughts and ideas for writing.

 Alphonso used the graphic organizer below to make a plan for writing his personal narrative.

Title: Niagara Falls

Beginning/Introduction → What? Who? When? Where? Why?

What happened?   We would be driving to see Niagara Falls but I wanted to play in the pool and take dogs for a walk.

Who did what?   Family and I visited my aunt and uncle.

When did it take place? summer

Where did it take place? Buffalo, New York

Why did it happen?   Aunt said we would be driving to see Niagra Falls.

Middle
   Aunt excited about Niagara Falls but not me
   short ride
   learned falls is on river between Lake Erie and Lake Ontario
   walked into park where you could look at falls
   level with the top of the falls – looked huge and sounded loud
   hypnotizing view
   elevator down to boat ride
   put on rain ponchos to ride *Maid of the Mist*
   mist, waves, loud crashing of waves, foam
   scary at first, imagining scary things happening
   relaxed and enjoyed the experience

End/Conclusion
   got wet even with ponchos
   went up on the elevator and looked down at boat
   boat looked like a toy
   glad I went
   real thing was so much better than photos

2. First Draft

This is Alphonso's personal narrative about an experience he'll never forget.

Niagara Falls

Have you ever heard of the *Maid of the Mist*? No, the Maid is not a lady who cleans houses, offices, or hotels for a living. No, the Mist is not a spray bottle of some kind of household cleaner. I'd never heard of the *Maid of the Mist* until Mom, Dad, Kate, and I visited Niagara Falls last summer.

Actually we were visiting Aunt Rosie and Uncle Leo in Buffalo New York. It all started when I was in there pool playing basketball with Dad and Uncle Leo. I did better in the pool than on the basketball court. My Mom and my Aunt came in the pool. We played girls against boys. My sister Kate made a lot of baskets, but not as many as I did. Later, I played fetch with their dogs whose names are dolly and poppy. Then, I watched the dogs play with their favorite toy, a plastic milk bottle. Aunt Rosie said she had a surprize for us.

"Today we're going to take a ride to Niagara Falls!" she exclaimed.

Aunt Rosie seemed really excited. I was not excited and I was disapointed. I wanted to keep playing in the pool and then take the dogs for a walk. I wanted to tell my aunt that I've seen loads of pictures of Niagara Falls, so I didn't think I wanted to go. I didn't say that because I knew my parents would say I was being rude. Besides Aunt Rosies smile showed me how happy she was. I just couldn't spoil that.

The ride to Niagara Falls was short. We parked and walked to a park where you could look at the falls. The park was level with the top of the falls. It was gigantic. It was loud. I couldn't stop looking. I was hypnotized. I learned that the falls is on the Niagara River between Lake Erie and Lake Ontario.

I remembered studying the Great Lakes in school. There are five Great Lakes. We used the acronym HOMES to remember them: Huron, Ontario, Michigan, Erie, and Superior. Niagara Falls was formed when glaciers melted. Water flows from four of the Great Lakes into the Niagara River and over the falls, and then the water flows into Lake Ontario to the Saint Lawrence river and empties into the Atlantic Ocean.

"who wants to ride on the *Maid of the Mist*?" Uncle Leo asked. I didn't know what he was talking about. Next, Uncle Leo waved us over to an elevator. We rode with a mess of other people down to the bottom of the falls. I found out the *Maid of the Mist* is a boat for people to ride to see the falls up close. The workers gave us rain ponchos to wear, but it wasn't raining. I started feeling scared when I got on the boat. As we moved away from the dock, the boat moved up and down with the waves. Looking up at the water falling was terrifying. Tons and tons of water were crashing down. It made me think of playing with toy boats when I was little. I would fill the sink with water and use the sprayer to squirt the water and make waves to move my boats. Of course, the falls was a billion times bigger than the kitchen sink and a billion times more powerful. The toor guide said about 3,160 tons of water flow over Niagara Falls every second.

I was frightened thinking the boat would float under the falls or even sink! Eventually, I relaxed and really enjoyed the experience.

Turns out we needed the ponchos because of the mist that hit us when the water fell. Even with the ponchos on, we got wet, but the tiny sprinkles of water felt good on my skin. We took the elevator up to the park. We stood and looked down where we had been. The *Maid of the Mist* looked like a toy boat in a bathtub. Boy, was I glad I went to Niagara Falls! The real thing was way better than looking at photos!

3. Revising Checklist

 Alphonso read his personal narrative and circled the answers to the following questions. Then he made changes to his personal narrative.

1. Does my title make the reader want to read my narrative?   Yes   No   (Maybe)
      Original Title: Niagara Falls
      Revised Title: The Real Thing

2. Does my first sentence capture the reader's interest?   Yes   No   (Maybe)

3. Is my writing organized with a beginning, a middle, and an end?   (Yes)   No   Maybe

4. Does my narrative make sense?   (Yes)   No   Maybe

5. Do I need to add more details?   (Yes)   No   Maybe
      Original Sentence in Second Paragraph:
         I did better in the pool than on the basketball court.
      Revised:
         I made more baskets in the pool than on the basketball court.

      Original Sentence in Fifth Paragraph:
         We parked and walked to a park where you can look at the falls.
      Revised:
         We parked and walked to Prospect Point park where you could look at the falls.

6. Do I need to remove or add any words or sentences?   (Yes)   No   Maybe
      Original Sentence in the Fifth Paragraph: It was gigantic.
      Revised: Niagara Falls was gigantic.

7. Does the narrative have my voice, the voice I use when I talk to my family and friends?
                                                                                 Yes   No   (Maybe)

      Original Sentence in Second Paragraph:
         Then, I watched the dogs play with their favorite toy, a plastic milk bottle.
      Revised:
         Then, I watched the dogs play with their favorite toy, believe it or not, a plastic milk bottle.

      Original Sentence in Fourth Paragraph:
         I was not excited and I was disapointed.
      Revised:
         I was not excited. I was disapointed.

8. Do I have my narrative separated into paragraphs?   (Yes)   No   Maybe

9. Did I write dialogue in its own paragraph?   Yes (No) Maybe
   Write in its Own Paragraph:
   "who wants to ride on the Maid of the Mist?" Uncle Leo asked.

10. Did I use transition words and phrases to connect one idea to the next?
                                                                 (Yes) No Maybe

11. Did I use sensory language, words that appeal to the reader's senses (sight, touch, taste, smell, hearing)?
                                                                 (Yes) No Maybe

12. Did I show the characters' actions, displays of emotion, dialogue, and thoughts so that the reader could draw his or her own conclusions about how the character is feeling, or did I simply tell the reader how the character is feeling?   Yes   No   (Maybe)
    Example:
    Tell: I was sick when I got to school.
    Show: I walked slowly into my classroom avoiding eye contact with my friends. When I got to my desk, I put my head down. The other kids were wearing sweaters and jackets, but I was sweating. To make matters worse, my head ached and it felt like the food in my stomach was not going to stay there for long. I walked up to my teacher and whispered. He handed me a clinic pass. As I walked out of the room, I hoped the nurse could get in touch with my mom or dad immediately.

13. Do I have a conclusion that reflects on my experience?   (Yes) No Maybe

Alphonso's friend read his personal narrative and answered the following questions.
1. Is there anything you'd like to know more about?
   "You were scared when you were on the boat. Then, you said you enjoyed the ride. What happened that made you more comfortable and relaxed on the boat?"

   Alphonso decided to change the eighth paragraph. He added the thoughts he had while riding on the *Maid of the Mist*. He realized that it was more interesting when he provided details about his thoughts instead of only saying he was frightened and then he enjoyed the ride. He felt he did a good job of showing, not telling.

   Original Eighth Paragraph: I was frightened thinking the boat would float under the falls or even sink! Eventually, I relaxed and really enjoyed the experience.
   Revised: I was frightened thinking the boat would float under the falls or even sink! Then, a funny thought popped into my head. When I looked at the falls, I could see Paul Bunyan as tall as the falls standing under the water with a bar of soap. I remembered reading that Bunyan carved out Niagara Falls so he could have a place to shower. Obviously, that was not true. It was a tall tale, but the memory made me smile. I relaxed and enjoyed riding on the *Maid of the Mist* with my family.

2. Is there anything you don't understand?"
   "No, there wasn't anything I did not understand.

3. Revised Draft

This is Alphonso's revision of his personal narrative.

The Real Thing

Have you ever heard of the *Maid of the Mist*? No, the Maid is not a lady who cleans houses, offices, or hotels for a living. No, the Mist is not a spray bottle of some kind of household cleaner. I'd never heard of the *Maid of the Mist* until Mom, Dad, Kate, and I visited Niagara Falls last summer.

Actually we were visiting Aunt Rosie and Uncle Leo in Buffalo New York. It all started when I was in there pool playing basketball with Dad and Uncle Leo. I made more baskets in the pool than on the basketball court. My Mom and my Aunt came in the pool. We played girls against boys. My sister Kate made a lot of baskets, but not as many as I did. Later, I played fetch with their dogs named dolly and poppy. Then, I watched the dogs play with their favorite toy, believe it or not, a plastic milk bottle. Aunt Rosie said she had a surprize for us.

"Today we're going to take a ride to Niagara Falls!" she exclaimed.

Aunt Rosie seemed really excited. I was not excited. I was disapointed. I wanted to keep playing in the pool, and then take the dogs for a walk. I wanted to tell my aunt that I've seen loads of pictures of Niagara Falls, so I didn't think I wanted to go. I didn't say that because I knew my parents would say I was being rude. Besides Aunt Rosies smile showed me how happy she was. I just couldn't spoil that.

The ride to Niagara Falls was short. We parked and walked to Prospect Point park where you could look at the falls. The park was level with the top of the falls. Niagara Falls was gigantic. It was loud. I couldn't stop looking. I was hypnotized. I learned that the falls is on the Niagara River between Lake Erie and Lake Ontario.

I remembered studying the Great Lakes in school. There are five Great Lakes. We used the acronym HOMES to remember them: Huron, Ontario, Michigan, Erie, and Superior. Niagara Falls was formed when glaciers melted. Water flows from four of the Great Lakes into the Niagara River and over the falls, and then the water flows into Lake Ontario to the Saint Lawrence river and empties into the Atlantic Ocean.

"who wants to go on the *Maid of the Mist*?" Uncle Leo asked.

I didn't know what he was talking about. Next, Uncle Leo waved us over to an elevator. We rode with a mess of other people down to the bottom of the falls. I found out the *Maid of the Mist* is a boat for people to ride to see the falls up close. The workers gave us rain ponchos to wear, but it wasn't raining. I started feeling scared when I got on the boat. As we moved away from the dock, the boat moved up and down with the waves. Looking up at the water falling was terrifying. Tons and tons of water were crashing down. It made me think of playing with toy boats when I was little. I would fill the sink with water and use the sprayer to squirt the water and make waves to move my boats. Of course, the falls was a billion times bigger than the kitchen sink and a billion times more powerful. The toor guide said about 3,160 tons of water flow over Niagara Falls every second.

I was frightened thinking the boat would float under the falls or even sink! Then, a funny thought popped into my head. When I looked at the falls, I could see Paul Bunyan, as tall as the falls, standing under the water with a bar of soap. I remembered reading that Bunyan carved out Niagara Falls so he could have a place to shower. Obviously, that was not true. It was a tall tale, but the memory made me smile. I relaxed and enjoyed riding the *Maid of the Mist* with my family.

Turns out we needed the ponchos because of the mist that hit us when the water fell. Even with the ponchos on, we got wet, but the tiny sprinkles of water felt good on my skin. We took the elevator up to the park. We stood and looked down where we had been. The *Maid of the Mist* looked like a toy boat in a bathtub. Boy, was I glad I went to Niagara Falls! The real thing was way better than looking at photos!

4. Editing Checklist

Alphonso reread and edited his personal narrative. He carefully looked for mistakes in spelling, capitalization, punctuation, word usage, and sentence structure.

Spelling

Alphonso checked for spelling errors and used a dictionary to correct them.

Original: surprize   Revised: surprise

Original: disapointed   Revised: disappointed

Original: toor   Revised: tour

Capitalization

Alphonso checked that he had capitalized:

- The first word of each sentence
- The word I
- Names of people and pets

  Original: dolly   Revised: Dolly

  Original: poppy   Revised: Poppy

- Words such as mom, dad, mother, father, aunt, uncle, when they are used as names

  Original: My **M**om   Revised: My **m**om

  Original: My **A**unt   Revised: my **a**unt

- Titles when they are used as names
- The first word of a quotation

  Original: "who wants to go on the *Maid of the Mist*?

  Revised: "**W**ho wants to go on the *maid of the Mist*?"

- Proper Nouns – nouns that name a specific person, place, or thing

  Original: Prospect Point **p**ark   Revised: Prospect Point **P**ark

  Original: Saint Lawrence **r**iver   Revised: Saint Lawrence **R**iver

- Days of the week and months of the year

4. Editing Checklist (continued)

Punctuation

Alphonso checked his punctuation: periods, question marks, exclamation points, commas, apostrophes, and quotation marks.

Original: Actually we were visiting Aunt Rosie and Uncle Leo in Buffalo New York.
Revised: Actually**,** we were visiting Aunt Rosie and Uncle Leo in Buffalo**,** New York.

Original: My sister Kate made a lot of baskets, but not as many as I did.
Revised: My sister**,** Kate**,** made a lot of baskets, but not as many as I did.

Original: Besides Aunt Rosies smile showed me how happy she was.
Revised: Besides**,** Aunt Rosie's smile showed me how happy she was.

Original: Turns out we needed the ponchos because of the mist that hit us when the water fell.
Revised: Turns out**,** we needed the ponchos because of the mist that hit us when the water fell.

Word Usage

Alphonso read his personal narrative aloud to see if he had used words correctly.

Original: It all started when I was in **there** pool playing basketball with Dad and Uncle Leo.
Revised: It all started when I was in **their** pool playing basketball with Dad and Uncle Leo.

Sentence Structure

Alphonso checked to make sure all of his sentences were complete thoughts and that he used simple, compound, and complex sentences. He decided that one sentence was too long. It was confusing.

Original Sentence: Water flows from four of the Great Lakes into the Niagara River and over the falls, and then the water flows into Lake Ontario to the Saint Lawrence River and empties into the Atlantic Ocean.
Revised Sentence: Water flows from four of the Great Lakes into the Niagara River and over the falls. Then, the water flows into Lake Ontario to the Saint Lawrence River. Finally, the water empties into the Atlantic Ocean.

5. Publishing

This is Alphonso's final copy of his personal narrative.

The Real Thing

Have you ever heard of the *Maid of the Mist*? No, the Maid is not a lady who cleans houses, offices, or hotels for a living. No, the Mist is not a spray bottle of some kind of household cleaner. I'd never heard of the *Maid of the Mist* until Mom, Dad, Kate, and I visited Niagara Falls last summer.

Actually, we were visiting Aunt Rosie and Uncle Leo in Buffalo, New York. It all started when I was in their pool playing basketball with Dad and Uncle Leo. I made more baskets in the pool than on the basketball court. My mom and my aunt came in the pool. We played girls against boys. My sister, Kate, made a lot of baskets, but not as many as I did. Later, I played fetch with their dogs named Dolly and Poppy. Then, I watched the dogs play with their favorite toy, believe it or not, a plastic milk bottle. Aunt Rosie said she had a surprise for us.

"Today we're going to take a ride to Niagara Falls!" she exclaimed.

Aunt Rosie seemed really excited. I was not excited. I was disappointed. I wanted to keep playing in the pool, and then take the dogs for a walk. I wanted to tell my aunt that I've seen loads of pictures of Niagara Falls, so I didn't think I wanted to go. I didn't say that because I knew my parents would say I was being rude. Besides, Aunt Rosie's smile showed me how happy she was. I just couldn't spoil that.

The ride to Niagara Falls was short. We parked and walked to Prospect Point Park where you could look at the falls. The park was level with the top of the falls. Niagara Falls was gigantic. It was loud. I couldn't stop looking. I was hypnotized. I learned that the falls is on the Niagara River between Lake Erie and Lake Ontario.

I remembered studying the Great Lakes in school. There are five Great Lakes. We used the acronym HOMES to remember them: Huron, Ontario, Michigan, Erie, and Superior. Niagara Falls was formed when glaciers melted. Water flows from four of the Great Lakes into the Niagara River and over the falls. Then, the water flows into Lake Ontario to the Saint Lawrence River. Finally, the water empties into the Atlantic Ocean.

"Who wants to go on the *Maid of the Mist*?" Uncle Leo asked.

I didn't know what he was talking about. Next, Uncle Leo waved us over to an elevator. We rode with a mess of other people down to the bottom of the falls. I found out the *Maid of the Mist* is a boat for people to ride to see the falls up close. The workers gave us rain ponchos to wear, but it wasn't raining. I started feeling scared when I got on the boat. As we moved away from the dock, the boat moved up and down with the waves. Looking up at the water falling was terrifying. Tons and tons of water were crashing down. It made me think of playing with toy boats when I was little. I would fill the sink with water and use the sprayer to squirt the water and make waves to move my boats. Of course, the falls was a billion times bigger than the kitchen sink and a billion times more powerful. The tour guide said about 3,160 tons of water flow over Niagara Falls every second.

I was frightened thinking the boat would float under the falls or even sink! Then, a funny thought popped into my head. When I looked at the falls, I could see Paul Bunyan, as tall as the falls, standing under the water with a bar of soap. I remembered reading that Bunyan carved out Niagara Falls so he could have a place to shower. Obviously, that was not true. It was a tall tale, but the memory made me smile. I relaxed and enjoyed riding the *Maid of the Mist* with my family.

Turns out, we needed the ponchos because of the mist that hit us when the water fell. Even with the ponchos on, we got wet, but the tiny sprinkles of water felt good on my skin. We took the elevator up to the park. We stood and looked down where we had been. The *Maid of the Mist* looked like a toy boat in a bathtub. Boy, was I glad I went to Niagara Falls! The real thing was way better than looking at photos!

1. Prewriting → Brainstorming

A **personal narrative** is a true story about an event or experience of the writer. Most personal narratives are told in the first person because the author is writing about himself or herself or a group that includes him or her.

First Person Pronouns
I, we, me, us, mine, our, ours

Write a personal narrative about an event or experience from your life or choose from the writing prompts on page 21. Refer to the Writing Process on pages 1 and 2 for information about writing a personal narrative. For an example of writing a personal narrative, see pages 3-11.

Brainstorm ideas for a topic for your personal narrative. Then circle the topic you have chosen.

What will the topic be for my personal narrative?

Write the topic you chose on the blank line below. Brainstorm ideas you have about your topic, and write them below your topic.

_____

1. Prewriting → Planning

Planning is the process of organizing thoughts and ideas for writing.

Use the graphic organizer below to make a plan for writing your personal narrative.

Title _____

Beginning/Introduction → What? Who? When? Where? Why?

What happened?   _____

Who did what?   _____

When did it take place? _____

Where did it take place? _____

Why did it happen?   _____

Middle

End/Conclusion

2. First Draft

Use your plans to help you write a first draft of your personal narrative.

_____

_____

_____

_____

_____

_____

_____

_____

_____

_____

_____

_____

_____

_____

_____

_____

_____

3. Revising Checklist

Authors revise the text to make their writing better.

Read the first draft of your personal narrative. Ask yourself the following questions and circle your answers. Use the information you gather from these questions to revise your writing. Write changes on your first draft using arrows (∧) to show where to add words or sentences. Draw a line through words or sentences you've decided to remove.

Niagara Falls

[∧]Ht was gigantic.

1. Does my title make the reader want to read my narrative?   Yes   No   Maybe

   Notes: _____

   _____

2. Does my first sentence capture the reader's interest?   Yes   No   Maybe

   Notes: _____

   _____

3. Is my narrative organized with a beginning, a middle, and an end?   Yes   No   Maybe

   Notes: _____

   _____

4. Does my narrative make sense?   Yes   No   Maybe

   Notes: _____

   _____

5. Do I need to add more details?   Yes   No   Maybe

   Notes: _____

   _____

6. Do I need to remove or add any words or sentences?   Yes   No   Maybe

   Notes: _____

   _____

7. Does the narrative have my voice, the voice I use when I talk to my family and friends?

                                                         Yes   No   Maybe

   Notes: _____

   _____

8. Do I have my story separated into paragraphs?   Yes   No   Maybe

   Notes: _____

   _____

9. Did I write dialogue in its own paragraph?   Yes   No   Maybe

   Notes: _____

   _____

10. Did I use transition words and phrases to connect one
    idea to the next?   Yes   No   Maybe

    Notes: _____

    _____

11. Did I use sensory language, words that appeal to the reader's
    senses (sight, touch, taste, smell, hearing)?   Yes   No   Maybe

    Notes: _____

    _____

12. Did I show the characters' actions, displays of emotion, dialogue, and thoughts so that the reader could draw his or her own conclusions about how the character is feeling, or did I simply tell the reader how the character is feeling?   Yes   No   Maybe
    Example:
    Tell: I was sick when I got to school.
    Show: I walked slowly into my classroom avoiding eye contact with my friends. When I got to my desk, I put my head down. The other kids were wearing sweaters and jackets, but I was sweating. To make matters worse, my head ached and it felt like the food in my stomach was not going to stay there for long. I walked up to my teacher and whispered. He handed me a clinic pass. As I walked out of the room, I hoped the nurse could get in touch with my mom or dad immediately.

    Notes: _____

    _____

13. Do I have a conclusion that reflects on my experience?   Yes   No   Maybe

    Notes: _____

    _____

Ask a friend or a family member to read your personal narrative and answer the following questions. Write the answers below the questions.

1. Is there anything you'd like to know more about?

    Notes: _____

    _____

2. Is there anything you don't understand?

    Notes: _____

    _____

3. Revised Draft

Use your notes to revise the first draft of your personal narrative.

_____

_____

_____

_____

_____

_____

_____

_____

_____

_____

_____

_____

_____

_____

_____

4. Editing Checklist

Reread and edit the revised draft of your personal narrative. Look carefully for mistakes in spelling, capitalization, punctuation, word usage, and sentence structure.

Spelling

Check for spelling errors. Use a dictionary to help correct spelling errors.

Circle words that are misspelled and write the correct spelling above.

Capitalization

Check to make sure you've capitalized:

- The first word of each sentence
- The word I
- Names of people and pets
- Words such as mom, dad, mother, father, aunt, uncle when they are used as names
- Titles when they are used with names
- The first word of a quotation
- Proper nouns–nouns that name a specific person, place, or thing
- Days of week and months of the year

Underline any letters that need to be capitalized.

Punctuation

Check your punctuation: periods, question marks, exclamation points, commas, apostrophes, and quotation marks.

Use an arrow (∧) with the correct punctuation mark above to show where it needs to be inserted.

Word Usage

Read your writing aloud to see if you've used words correctly.

Put a line through words used incorrectly and write the correction above.

Sentence Structure

Check to make sure all of your sentences are complete thoughts. If all of your sentences are simple sentences, try to make some compound or complex.

Put lines through words you do not want to use. Use arrows (∧) to show where words should be added.

5. Publishing

Write the final copy of your personal narrative with the changes from your editing and revising.

_____

_____

_____

_____

_____

_____

_____

_____

_____

_____

_____

_____

_____

_____

_____

_____

_____

_____

Personal Narrative Writing Prompts

1. Think about a favorite holiday memory. Write about what happened.

2. Write a true story about a fun or interesting experience.

3. Write a story about an experience you'll never forget.

4. Think about a trip you took. It could be far away or nearby. Write about what happened.

5. Write about a time when you felt embarrassed.

6. Think about a time when you felt scared. Write about what happened.

7. Think of a time when you had fun with a friend. Write about what happened.

8. Write about a time someone said you did a great job.

9. Write about one of your saddest memories.

10. Think about a time you had fun visiting a relative. Write about what happened.

11. Write a true story about an experience you've had with an animal.

12. Think about a time when you helped someone or someone helped you. Write about what happened.

13. Write about a time you felt happy.

14. Write about a time you felt proud of yourself.

15. Write about a hobby or activity you enjoy.

Personal Narrative Writing Rubric

Organization	Voice and Word Choice	Language Arts Standards	Sentence Structure
Score 4 → 90%-100% A real situation is established with a narrator and/or characters and a setting. The first sentence captures the reader's interest. Events unfold naturally with a beginning, middle, and end. A strong conclusion from the narrated experience is provided.	Score 4 → 90%-100% The writer's voice creates interest and enjoyment for the reader. The experience is portrayed using dialogue and descriptions that develop experiences and events to show the response of characters to situations. The writer's personality and feelings are expressed in the writing.	Score 4 → 90%-100% Writing shows a strong command of grade level language arts standards. The writer uses correct capitalization, punctuation, and spelling for the most part.	Score 4 → 90%-100% Sentences are varied: simple, compound, and complex. Sentences are well-developed and are interesting to the reader.
Score 3 → 80%-89% A real situation is established with a narrator and/or characters and a setting. The first sentence may capture the reader's interest. Events unfold naturally with a beginning, middle, and end. A conclusion from the narrated experience is provided.	Score 3 → 80%-89% The writer's voice creates some interest and enjoyment for the reader. The experience is portrayed using some dialogue and descriptions that develop experiences and events to show the response of characters to situations. Some of the writer's personality and feelings are expressed in the writing.	Score 3 → 80%-89% Writing shows a good command of grade level language arts standards. The few errors in capitalization, punctuation, and spelling do not interfere with understanding.	Score 3 → 80%-89% Sentences are varied for the most part. Sentences are complete and contain details that are interesting to the reader.
Score 2 → 70%-79% A real situation is established with a narrator and/or characters and a setting. Writing is somewhat organized, but lacks a complete sequence of events that unfolds naturally. A conclusion is provided.	Score 2 → 70%-79% The writer's voice is usually evident. Writing needs more details. Writing shows some feeling. The writer's personality and feelings are vaguely expressed in the writing.	Score 2 → 70%-79% Writing shows some command of grade level language arts standards. Errors in capitalization, punctuation, and spelling may interfere with understanding.	Score 2 → 70%-79% Sentences are simple with few details. Some sentences are weak or awkward.
Score 1 → Below 70% A real situation with characters and a setting may be presented. Writing shows little or no evidence of organization. No conclusion or a weak conclusion is provided.	Score 1 → Below 70% The writer's voice is weak. Few details are provided to interest the reader. The writing is flat. The reader is not engaged.	Score 1 → Below 70% Writing shows little or no command of grade level language arts standards. Errors in capitalization, punctuation, and spelling interfere with understanding.	Score 1 → Below 70% Sentences are often incomplete or confusing.

Story Narrative

A **story narrative** is a story imagined by the writer. The writer must establish a situation, introduce characters, and organize an event sequence that unfolds naturally. The characters are presented with a problem or conflict that is resolved in the course of the story.

Example: Long ago, a dragon named Toby lived in a small forest. There were many animals that made the forest their home. Unfortunately, these animals did not want to be friends with Toby, because he could shoot fire out of his mouth. One day, a big cougar showed up in the forest. The small animals were very afraid because they did not want to be cougar food. Toby saw the cougar and shot some fire out of his mouth. The cougar ran out of the small forest. Toby was a hero and the other animals became his friends.

5-Step Writing Process

1. **Prewriting - Time to Think**

2. **First Draft - Time to Write**

3. **Revising - Time to Improve Your Writing**

4. **Editing - Time to Make Corrections**

5. **Publishing - Time to Share**

Story Narrative Writing Process

Use these steps to write a story narrative.

---

1. Prewriting - Time to Think
- Decide on a topic to write about.
- Brainstorm—discuss your topic with others.
  - Ask: What? Who? When? Where? Why?
- Consider who will read your writing.
- Gather information about your topic.
- Organize the information—make a plan.
  - Beginning (Introduction)
  - Middle
  - End (Conclusion)

▼

2. First Draft - Time to Write
- Use complete sentences and paragraphs to organize your information.
- Have others read it and offer suggestions.

▼

3. Revising - Time to Improve Your Writing
- Read what you have written and make changes if needed, keeping in mind what others suggested.
  - Add descriptive words.
  - Add more detail.

▼

4. Editing - Time to Make Corrections
- Make sure you use complete sentences, correct spelling, punctuation, and capitalization.

▼

5. Publishing - Time to Share
- Read it aloud in class.
- Send copies to friends or relatives.

1. Prewriting → Brainstorming

A **story narrative** is a story imagined by the writer. The writer must establish a situation, introduce characters, and organize an event sequence that unfolds naturally. The characters are presented with a problem or conflict that is resolved in the course of the story.

 Pam was given a writing prompt for a story narrative: Imagine an alien is on Earth to help you solve a problem. Write a story about how the alien helped you.

Pam brainstormed and wrote down ideas she had for a topic for her story narrative. Then she chose one topic.

What will the topic be for my story narrative?
The alien could help me…

improve my tennis swing	clean my room
teach my dog new tricks	learn to roller skate
learn to play a guitar	with my science project
understand equations in math	do my chores

Pam brainstormed ideas about an alien helping her with math to get some ideas on paper before organizing them in the planning step of the writing process.

Understand Equations in Math	
problems with math equations	teacher wants to see me before class
Mr. Roscoe Matt M. Mattix (alien)	meet alien who is a math whiz
Rob	alien helps without anyone knowing
already had help at home	alien sits on eraser
was tutored at school	alien doesn't help with tests or quizzes
afraid of failing math	alien becomes a friend

1. Prewriting → Planning

Planning is the process of organizing thoughts and ideas for writing.

Pam used the story map below to make a plan for writing her story narrative.

Title: Math Magic

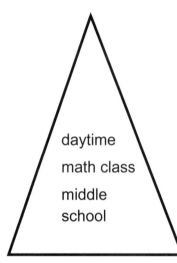

daytime

math class

middle

school

Settings

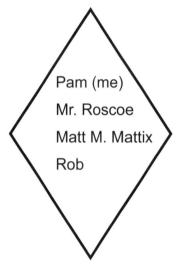

Pam (me)

Mr. Roscoe

Matt M. Mattix

Rob

Characters

I used to like math, but I'm having lots of problems understanding equations.

Problem/Conflict

Mr. Roscoe, my math teacher, met me at the door to math class. He talked to me about improving my math grades. Mr. Roscoe said he had a special tutor who could help me this week.

Beginning/Introduction

He gave me a tiny pencil box shaped like a rocket. I went to my desk and opened the box. Out jumped a tiny alien. No one seemed to see him except me. He helped me when we had practice work.

Middle

I was the only one who could see or hear the alien. He heard my thoughts as I tried to solve equations. He helped me understand. He stayed with me during math class for a week.

End/Conclusion

2. First Draft

This is Pam's story narrative about an alien who helps her with understanding math equations.

Math Magic

I saw Mr. Roscoe standing at the door of my math class. Math used to be one of my favorite subjects. Now, I dreaded math class. Mr. Roscoe said hello and told me to come in and have a seat. He wanted to talk to me.

"Pam," he said, "I know your having trouble with equations. I have something I hope will be helpful to you. Take this pencil box. You may use it every day this week during math class, but you have to give it back to me at the end of each class. Also, do not talk out loud when you use it."

Mr. Roscoe held out a pencil box shaped like a rocket.   Why would I be talking to a pencil box? Mr. Roscoe is a good guy. He's always trying to find ways to help us. I thanked him and took the pencil box to my seat. I opened the box. I found pencils and a pink eraser. Then a tiny alien popped out of the box. He sat on the pink eraser.

The alien said, "My name is Matt M. Mattix. I'm here to help you with math. My planet is full of math experts, so we travel to other planets helping others with math."

I realised that the other kids couldn't see Matt at all. I opened my mouth to say something to Matt, but I remembered what Mr. Roscoe said. I thought about how it would be great to have my own personel tutor. I thought about equations, and how I don't like letters mixed up with numbers.

Matt said, "I'm glad your happy that I'll be helping you. Honestly, the first thing you have to do is change the way you're thinking. You need to accept the fact that equations contain letters. Once you open your mind about that, you'll be able to start understanding the meaning of equations. Compare it to reading a fantasy story. What if you continuously said, "That can't happen! That's crazy!"? You would not like the story. You would not enjoy the story. However, if you accepted the world the author created, you'd understand the story and probably enjoy it."

I couldn't believe it! Matt heard me thinking. What he said made cents. I did have to accept numbers mixed with letters in equations.

"Now that you've accepted letters mixed with numbers, we'll start solving problems! Let's start with simple equations. In fact let's start with objects."

Matt took out some M&M's. He put a group of five M&M's on my desk. He used a dry erase marker to write a plus sign. Then, he told me to cover my eyes. When I opened them, I saw a white paper, an equal sign, and a group of fourteen M&M's.

Matt said, "There are M&M's under the white paper. What is it you don't know here?"

I answered, "I don't know how many M&M's are under the white paper."

"So that is the unknown. A letter stands for the unknown in equations. In other words, we could write an equation for this, $5 + X = 14$.   It's like a mystery to solve. What do you think?"

"I know the answer is 9, because if you count up from 5 to 14, it takes 9 to reach 14."

"Fantastic! There is another way to solve this problem. Remember, when you have an equal sign, both sides have the same value. If you subtract the same number from both sides, the sides will still be equal. If you add the same number to both sides, the sides will still be equal. If you want to find the value of X in 5 + X = 14, you could subtract 5 from both sides. What would you get?"

Matt handed me the marker and the eraser. I subtracted 5 from the first side and all that was left was X. I subtracted 5 from the other side and got 9. I wrote X = 9.

Matt said, "This helps a lot when you have larger numbers such as 80 + X = 140."

"I get it!" I said. "Subtract 80 from both sides! What you get is X = 60!"

I was thrilled when Matt let me eat the M&M's! Then, we solved ten more equations. No one seemed to notice me eating M&M's. It was almost like I was dreaming. At the end of class, I waited until all the kids left the room. I put Matt in the rocket pencil box and gave it to Mr. Roscoe.

"Did Matt help you out at all?" Mr. Roscoe asked.

"Yes, he did. As soon as I had a question in my head, he explained so that I could understand. Equations are like solving a mystery! I like mysteries!"

Mr. Roscoe smiled. I leaned toward the pencil box and thanked Matt. I wished that Matt could go home with me. He could help me with my math homework.

Matt and I worked on equations all week. Each day the equations were more difficult. Matt was careful to help me just enough. He'd give me just enough of a hint or tip so that I could continue and solve the equation. That week, we had one quiz and one test. Matt sat at the edge of my desk with his legs swinging back and forth. He looked out the window. He looked at the other kids. He did not help me at all during the quiz or the test.

I wanted to take Matt home with me, but he had to stay with Mr. Roscoe. I said goodbye to Matt. On monday morning I missed Matt. It was so quiet in the classroom till my freind Rob burst out laughing. Mr. Roscoe looked at Rob and raised his left eyebrow. Rob stopped laughing imediately. Mr. Roscoe glanced my way and winked. As he turned to walk back to his desk, I noticed the back of his shirt said "Math Expert." Could my teacher be an alien from outer space?

3. Revising Checklist

 Pam read her story narrative and circled the answers to the following questions. Then she made revisions to her story narrative.

1. Does my title make the reader want to read my narrative?   (Yes)   No   Maybe

2. Does my first sentence capture the reader's interest?   Yes   No   (Maybe)
   Original First Sentence:
       I saw Mr. Roscoe standing at the door of my math class.
   Revised:
       When I got the message that my math teacher, Mr. Roscoe, wanted to see me before class, I was not happy.

3. Is my narrative organized with a beginning, a middle, and an end?   (Yes)   No   Maybe

4. Does my narrative make sense?   (Yes)   No   Maybe

5. Do I need to add more details?   Yes   (No)   Maybe

6. Do I need to remove or add any words or sentences?   Yes   (No)   Maybe

7. Does the narrative have my voice, the voice I use when I talk to my family and friends?
                                                            (Yes)   No   Maybe

8. Do I have my narrative separated into paragraphs?   (Yes)   No   Maybe

9. Did I write dialogue in its own paragraph?   (Yes)   No   Maybe

10. Did I use transition words and phrases to connect one idea to the next?
                                                            Yes   No   (Maybe)

    Original First Sentence in the Last Paragraph:
        I wanted to take Matt home with me, but he had to stay with Mr. Roscoe.
    Revised:
        After class on Friday, I wanted to take Matt home with me, but he had to stay with Mr. Roscoe.

11. Did I use sensory language, words that appeal to the reader's senses (sight, touch, taste, smell, hearing)?   Yes   No   (Maybe)
    Original Paragraph:
        I was thrilled when Matt let me eat the M&M's! Then, we solved ten more equations. No one seemed to notice me eating M&M's. It was almost like I was dreaming. At the end of class, I waited until all the kids left the room. I put Matt in the rocket pencil box and gave it to Mr. Roscoe.

Revised:

I was thrilled when Matt let me eat the M&M's! Then, we solved ten more equations. No one seemed to notice me eating M&M's. I thought for sure they could smell the chocolaty goodness and hear the crunch of the candies in my mouth. It was almost like I was dreaming. At the end of class, I waited until all the kids left the room. I put Matt in the rocket pencil box and gave it to Mr. Roscoe.

12. Did I use expressive dialogue to show characters' emotions and attitudes, instead of <u>simply</u> telling readers how to feel?   Yes   No

Original Fifth Paragraph:

I realised that the other kids couldn't see Matt at all. I opened my mouth to say something to Matt, but I remembered what Mr. Roscoe said. I thought about how it would be great to have my own personal tutor. I thought about equations and how I don't like letters mixed up with numbers.

Revised:

I looked around. I thought the other kids would be staring at Matt. The boy sitting next to me looked right at me. Matt stood up and walked across my desk. Next Matt started doing jumping jacks. The other kids were clueless. They paid no attention. I realised that the other kids couldn't see Matt at all.

13. Do I have a conclusion to my narrative?   Yes   No   Maybe

 Pam's friend read her story narrative and answered the following questions.

1. Is there anything you'd like to know more about?
   "What planet is Matt from? How did he get to Earth?"

   Original Last Paragraph:

   I wanted to take Matt home with me, but he had to stay with Mr. Roscoe. I said goodbye to Matt. On monday morning I missed Matt. It was so quiet in the class room till my freind Rob burst out laughing. Mr. Roscoe looked at Rob and raised his left eyebrow. Rob stopped laughing imediately. Mr. Roscoe glanced my way and winked. As he turned to walk back to his desk, I noticed the back of his shirt said "Math Expert." Could my teacher be an alien from outer space?

   Revised:

   After class on Friday, I wanted to take Matt home with me, but he had to stay with Mr. Roscoe. **I kept wondering what planet he was from and how he got to earth. Mr. Roscoe said Matt was on a secret mission and couldn't talk about it. Sadly**, I said goodbye to Matt. On monday morning, I missed Matt. It was so quiet in the class room till my friend Rob burst out laughing. Mr. Roscoe looked at Rob and raised his left eyebrow. Rob stopped laughing imediately. Mr. Roscoe glanced my way and winked. As he turned to walk back to his desk, I noticed the back of his shirt said "Math Expert." Could my teacher be an alien from outer space?

2. Is there anything you don't understand?
   "No, I understood."

3. Revised Draft

 This is Pam's revision of her story narrative.

Math Magic

When I got the message that my math teacher, Mr. Roscoe, wanted to talk to me before class, I was not happy. Math used to be one of my favorite subjects. Now, I dreaded math class. Mr. Roscoe said hello and told me to come in and have a seat.

"Pam!" he said, "I know your having trouble with equations. I have something I hope will be helpful to you. Take this pencil box. You may use it every day this week during math class, but you have to give it back to me at the end of each class. Also, do not talk out loud when you use it."

Mr. Roscoe held out a pencil box shaped like a rocket. Why would I be talking to a pencil box? Mr. Roscoe is a good guy. He's always trying to find ways to help us. I thanked him and took the pencil box to my seat. I opened the box. I found pencils and a pink eraser. Then a tiny alien popped out of the box. He sat on the pink eraser.

The alien said, "My name is Matt M. Mattix. I'm here to help you with math. My planet is full of math experts, so we travel to other planets helping others with math."

I looked around. I thought the other kids would be staring at Matt. The boy sitting next to me looked right at me. Matt stood up and walked across my desk. Next Matt started doing jumping jacks. The other kids were clueless. They paid no attention. I realised that the other kids couldn't see Matt at all. I opened my mouth to say something to Matt, but I remembered what Mr. Roscoe said. I thought about how it would be great to have my own personel tutor. I thought about equations, and how I don't like letters mixed up with numbers.

Matt said, "I'm glad your happy that I'll be helping you. Honestly, the first thing you have to do is change the way you're thinking. You need to accept the fact that equations contain letters. Once you open your mind about that, you'll be able to start understanding the meaning of equations. Compare it to reading a fantasy story. What if you continuously said, "That can't happen! That's crazy!"? You would not like the story. You would not enjoy the story. However, if you accepted the world the author created, you'd understand the story and probably enjoy it."

I couldn't believe it! Matt heard me thinking. What he said made cents. I did have to accept numbers mixed with letters in equations.

"Now that you've accepted letters mixed with numbers, we'll start solving problems! Let's start with simple equations. In fact let's start with objects."

Matt took out some M&M's. He put a group of five M&M's on my desk. He used a dry erase marker to write a plus sign. Then, he told me to cover my eyes. When I opened them, I saw a white paper, an equal sign, and a group of fourteen M&M's.

Matt said, "There are M&M's under the white paper. What is it you don't know here?"

I answered, "I don't know how many M&M's are under the white paper."

"So that is the unknown. A letter stands for the unknown in equations. In other words, we could write an equation for this, 5 + X = 14. It's like a mystery to solve. What do you think?"

"I know the answer is 9, because if you count up from 5 to 14, it takes 9 to reach 14."

"Fantastic! There is another way to solve this problem. Remember, when you have an equal sign, both sides have the same value. If you subtract the same number from both sides, the sides will still be equal. If you add the same number to both sides, the sides will still be equal. If you want to find the value of X in 5 + X = 14, you could subtract 5 from both sides. What would you get?"

Matt handed me the marker and the eraser. I subtracted 5 from the first side and all that was left was X. I subtracted 5 from the other side and got 9. I wrote X = 9.

Matt said, "This helps a lot when you have larger numbers such as 80 + X = 140."

"I get it!" I said. "Subtract 80 from both sides! What you get is X = 60!"

I was thrilled when Matt let me eat the M&M's! Then, we solved ten more equations. No one seemed to notice me eating M&M's. I thought for sure they could smell the chocolaty goodness and hear the crunch of the candies in my mouth. It was almost like I was dreaming. At the end of class, I waited until all the kids left the room. I put Matt in the rocket pencil box and gave it to Mr. Roscoe.

"Did Matt help you out at all?" Mr. Roscoe asked.

"Yes, he did. As soon as I had a question in my head, he explained so that I could understand. Equations are like solving a mystery! I like mysteries!"

Mr. Roscoe smiled. I leaned toward the pencil box and thanked Matt. I wished that Matt could go home with me. He could help me with my math homework.

Matt and I worked on equations all week. Each day the equations were more difficult. Matt was careful to help me just enough. He'd give me just enough of a hint or tip so that I could continue and solve the equation. That week, we had one quiz and one test. Matt sat at the edge of my desk with his legs swinging back and forth. He looked out the window. He looked at the other kids. He did not help me at all during the quiz or the test.

After class on Friday, I wanted to take Matt home with me, but he had to stay with Mr. Roscoe. I kept wondering what planet he was from and how he got to earth. Mr. Roscoe said Matt was on a secret mission and couldn't talk about it. Sadly, I said goodbye to Matt. On monday morning, I missed Matt. It was so quiet in the classroom till my freind Rob burst out laughing. Mr. Roscoe looked at Rob and raised his left eyebrow. Rob stopped laughing imediately. Mr. Roscoe glanced my way and winked. As he turned to walk back to his desk, I noticed the back of his shirt said "Math Expert." Could my teacher be an alien from outer space?

4. Editing Checklist

 Pam reread and edited her story narrative. She carefully looked for mistakes in spelling, capitalization, punctuation, word usage, and sentence structure.

Spelling
Pam checked for spelling errors and used a dictionary to correct them.

Original: realised	Revised: realized
Original: personel	Revised: personal
Original: freind	Revised: friend
Original: imediately	Revised: immediately

Capitalization
Pam checked that she had capitalized:
- The first word of each sentence
- The word I
- Names of people and pets
- Words such as mom, dad, mother, father, aunt, uncle, when they are used as names
- Titles when they are used as names
- The first word of a quotation
- Proper Nouns – nouns that name a specific person, place, or thing

  Original: **e**arth   Revised: **E**arth
- Days of the week and months of the year

  Original: **m**onday   Revised: **M**onday

Punctuation
Pam checked her punctuation: periods, question marks, exclamation points, commas, apostrophes, and quotation marks.

Original: Then a tiny alien popped out of the box.
Revised: Then, a tiny alien popped out of the box.

Original: Next Matt started doing jumping jacks.
Revised: Next, Matt started doing jumping jacks.

Original: In fact let's start with objects.
Revised: In fact, let's start with objects.

Original: It was so quiet in the classroom till my friend Rob burst out laughing.
Revised: It was so quiet in the classroom till my friend, Rob, burst out laughing.

Word Usage

Pam read her writing aloud to see if she had used words correctly.

Original: I know **your** having trouble with equations
Revised: I know **you're** having trouble with equations

Original: I'm glad **your** happy that I'll be helping you.
Revised: I'm glad **you're** happy that I'll be helping you.

Original: What he said made **cents**.
Revised: What he said made **sense**.

Sentence Structure

Pam checked to make sure all of her sentences were complete thoughts and that she used simple, compound, and complex sentences.   Pam decided not to change any sentences.

5. Publishing

 Pam wrote her final copy with the changes from her revising and editing.

Math Magic

When I got the message that my math teacher, Mr. Roscoe, wanted to talk to me before class, I was not happy. Math used to be one of my favorite subjects. Now, I dreaded math class. Mr. Roscoe said hello and told me to come in and have a seat.

"Pam!" he said, "I know you're having trouble with equations. I have something I hope will be helpful to you. Take this pencil box. You may use it every day this week during math class, but you have to give it back to me at the end of each class. Also, do not talk out loud when you use it."

Mr. Roscoe held out a pencil box shaped like a rocket. Why would I be talking to a pencil box? Mr. Roscoe is a good guy. He's always trying to find ways to help us. I thanked him and took the pencil box to my seat. I opened the box. I found pencils and a pink eraser. Then, a tiny alien popped out of the box. He sat on the pink eraser.

The alien said, "My name is Matt M. Mattix. I'm here to help you with math. My planet is full of math experts, so we travel to other planets helping others with math."

I looked around. I thought the other kids would be staring at Matt. The boy sitting next to me looked right at me. Matt stood up and walked across my desk. Next, Matt started doing jumping jacks. The other kids were clueless. They paid no attention. I realized that the other kids couldn't see Matt at all. I opened my mouth to say something to Matt, but I remembered what Mr. Roscoe said. I thought about how it would be great to have my own personal tutor. I thought about equations, and how I don't like letters mixed up with numbers.

Matt said, "I'm glad you're happy that I'll be helping you. Honestly, the first thing you have to do is change the way you're thinking. You need to accept the fact that equations contain letters. Once you open your mind about that, you'll be able to start understanding the meaning of equations. Compare it to reading a fantasy story. What if you continuously said, "That can't happen! That's crazy!"? You would not like the story. You would not enjoy the story. However, if you accepted the world the author created, you'd understand the story and probably enjoy it."

I couldn't believe it! Matt heard me thinking. What he said made sense. I did have to accept numbers mixed with letters in equations.

"Now that you've accepted letters mixed with numbers, we'll start solving problems! Let's start with simple equations. In fact, let's start with objects."

Matt took out some M&M's. He put a group of five M&M's on my desk. He used a dry erase marker to write a plus sign. Then, he told me to cover my eyes. When I opened them, I saw a white paper, an equal sign, and a group of fourteen M&M's.

Matt said, "There are M&M's under the white paper. What is it you don't know here?"

I answered, "I don't know how many M&M's are under the white paper."

"So that is the unknown. A letter stands for the unknown in equations. In other words, we could write an equation for this, $5 + X = 14$. It's like a mystery to solve. What do you think?"

"I know the answer is 9, because if you count up from 5 to 14, it takes 9 to reach 14."

"Fantastic! There is another way to solve this problem. Remember, when you have an equal sign, both sides have the same value. If you subtract the same number from both sides, the sides will still be equal. If you add the same number to both sides, the sides will still be equal. If you want to find the value of X in 5 + X = 14, you could subtract 5 from both sides. What would you get?"

Matt handed me the marker and the eraser. I subtracted 5 from the first side and all that was left was X. I subtracted 5 from the other side and got 9. I wrote X = 9.

Matt said, "This helps a lot when you have larger numbers such as 80 + X = 140."

"I get it!" I said. "Subtract 80 from both sides! What you get is X = 60!"

I was thrilled when Matt let me eat the M&M's! Then, we solved ten more equations. No one seemed to notice me eating M&M's. I thought for sure they could smell the chocolaty goodness and hear the crunch of the candies in my mouth. It was almost like I was dreaming. At the end of class, I waited until all the kids left the room. I put Matt in the rocket pencil box and gave it to Mr. Roscoe.

"Did Matt help you out at all?" Mr. Roscoe asked.

"Yes, he did. As soon as I had a question in my head, he explained so that I could understand. Equations are like solving a mystery! I like mysteries!"

Mr. Roscoe smiled. I leaned toward the pencil box and thanked Matt. I wished that Matt could go home with me. He could help me with my math homework.

Matt and I worked on equations all week. Each day the equations were more difficult. Matt was careful to help me just enough. He'd give me just enough of a hint or tip so that I could continue and solve the equation. That week, we had one quiz and one test. Matt sat at the edge of my desk with his legs swinging back and forth. He looked out the window. He looked at the other kids. He did not help me at all during the quiz or the test.

After class on Friday, I wanted to take Matt home with me, but he had to stay with Mr. Roscoe. I kept wondering what planet he was from and how he got to Earth. Mr. Roscoe said Matt was on a secret mission and couldn't talk about it. Sadly, I said goodbye to Matt. On Monday morning, I missed Matt. It was so quiet in the classroom till my friend, Rob, burst out laughing. Mr. Roscoe looked at Rob and raised his left eyebrow. Rob stopped laughing immediately. Mr. Roscoe glanced my way and winked. As he turned to walk back to his desk, I noticed the back of his shirt said "Math Expert." Could my teacher be an alien from outer space?

1. Prewriting → Brainstorming

A **story narrative** is a story imagined by the writer. The writer must establish a situation, introduce characters, and organize an event sequence that unfolds naturally. The characters are presented with a problem or conflict that is resolved in the course of the story.

Write a story narrative about an imagined event or experience or choose from the writing prompts on page 46. Refer to the Writing Process on pages 23 and 24 for information about writing a story narrative. For an example of writing a story narrative, see pages 25-36.

Brainstorm ideas for a topic for your story narrative. Then circle the topic you have chosen.

What will the topic be for my story narrative?

Write the topic you chose on the blank line below. Brainstorm ideas you have about your topic, and write them below your topic.

_____

1. Prewriting → Planning

Planning is the process of organizing thoughts and ideas for writing.

Use the story map below to make a plan for writing your story narrative.

Title: _____

Settings   **Characters**   **Problem/Conflict**

Beginning/Introduction   **Middle**   **End/Conclusion**

2. First Draft

Use your plans to help you write a first draft of your story narrative.

_____

_____

_____

_____

_____

_____

_____

_____

_____

_____

_____

_____

_____

_____

_____

_____

3. Revising Checklist

Authors revise the text to make their writing better.

Read the first draft of your story narrative. Ask yourself the following questions and circle your answers. Use the information you gather from these questions to revise your writing. Write changes on your first draft using arrows (∧) to show where to add words or sentences. Draw a line through words or sentences you've decided to remove.

Niagara Falls

∧ H̶t̶ was gigantic.

1. Does my title make the reader want to read my narrative?   Yes   No   Maybe

   Notes: _____

   _____

2. Does my first sentence capture the reader's interest?   Yes   No   Maybe

   Notes: _____

   _____

3. Is my narrative organized with a beginning, a middle, and an end?   Yes   No   Maybe

   Notes: _____

   _____

4. Does my narrative make sense?   Yes   No   Maybe

   Notes: _____

   _____

5. Do I need to add more details?   Yes   No   Maybe

   Notes: _____

   _____

6. Do I need to remove or add any words or sentences?   Yes   No   Maybe

    Notes: _____

    _____

7. Does the narrative have my voice, the voice I use when I talk to my family and friends?

                                                               Yes   No   Maybe

    Notes: _____

    _____

8. Do I have my narrative separated into paragraphs?   Yes   No   Maybe

    Notes: _____

    _____

9. Did I write dialogue in its own paragraph?   Yes   No   Maybe

    Notes: _____

    _____

10. Did I use transition words, phrases, and clauses to connect one
    idea to the next?   Yes   No   Maybe

    Notes: _____

    _____

11. Did I use sensory language, words that appeal to the readers'
    senses (sight, touch, taste, smell, hearing)?   Yes   No   Maybe

    Notes: _____

    _____

12. Did I use expressive dialogue to show characters' emotions and attitudes, instead of simply telling readers how to feel?   Yes   No   Maybe

   Example:

   Tell: Mary was sick when she got to school.

   Show: Mary walked slowly into the classroom not talking to any of her friends. She put her head on her desk. Then, she managed to walk up to Mr. Baxter and whisper. He took out a clinic pass and gave it to Mary. She walked out of the room.

   Notes: _____

   _____

13. Do I have a conclusion to my narrative?   Yes   No   Maybe

   Notes: _____

   _____

Ask a friend or a family member to read your story narrative and answer the following questions. Write the answers below the questions.

1. Is there anything you'd like to know more about?

   Notes: _____

   _____

   _____

2. Is there anything you don't understand?

   Notes: _____

   _____

   _____

3. Revised Draft

Use your notes to revise the first draft of your story narrative.

_____

_____

_____

_____

_____

_____

_____

_____

_____

_____

_____

_____

_____

_____

_____

_____

_____

4. Editing Checklist

Reread and edit the revised draft of your story narrative. Look carefully for mistakes in spelling, capitalization, punctuation, word usage, and sentence structure.

Spelling

Check for spelling errors. Use a dictionary to help correct spelling errors.

Circle words that are misspelled and write the correct spelling above.

Capitalization

Check to make sure you've capitalized:
- The first word of each sentence
- The word **I**
- Names of people and pets
- Words like mom, dad, mother, father, aunt, uncle when they are used as names
- Titles when they are used with names
- The first word of a quotation
- Proper nouns–nouns that name a specific person, place, or thing
- Days of week and months of the year

Underline any letters that need to be capitalized.

Punctuation

Check your punctuation: periods, question marks, exclamation points, commas, apostrophes, and quotation marks.

Use an arrow (∧) with the correct punctuation mark above to show where it needs to be inserted.

Word Usage

Read your writing aloud to see if you've used words correctly.

Put a line through words used incorrectly and write the correction above.

Sentence Structure

Check to make sure all of your sentences are complete thoughts. If all of your sentences are simple sentences, try to make some compound or complex.

Put lines through words you do not want to use. Use arrows (∧) to show where words should be added.

5. Publishing

Write the final copy of your story narrative with the changes from your editing and revising.

_____

_____

_____

_____

_____

_____

_____

_____

_____

_____

_____

_____

_____

_____

_____

_____

_____

_____

Story Narrative Writing Prompts

1. You wake up one morning, and you are invisible. Write a story about that day.

2. Imagine you come home from school, and your dog is jumping on you and wagging his tail. You say, "How are you doing, Little Buddy?" Your dog answers, "I'm good, but I could use a biscuit!" Write a story about the day your dog could talk.

3. Write a story about the day you discovered you could fly.

4. Write a story about two friends who have an adventure at the neighborhood park.

5. Pretend you won the lottery. Write a story about that day. What did you decide to do with the money?

6. Your friend's dog caused problems at his or her birthday party. Write about what happened.

7. Your friend wants you to go on a roller coaster at the amusement park. You are terrified. Write about the day you finally went on the roller coaster.

8. Write a story about the day you visited the science museum and the dinosaurs came to life.

9. Write a story about the day you left your homework at home.

10. You wake up one morning, and the snow is falling so hard that you see a blanket of white when you look out the window. You wonder if you will have school. Write about what happened that day.

11. You are invited to two birthday parties on the same day. Write a story about what happened.

12. Write a story about two friends who find a turtle on the sidewalk.

13. Write a story about the day an animal escaped from the zoo.

14. Pretend you opened your own restaurant. Write about what the restaurant looks like, what kind of food you serve, and who works at the restaurant.

15. Write a story about two friends having a fun day at the beach.

Story Narrative Writing Rubric

Organization	Voice and Word Choice	Language Arts Standards	Sentence Structure
Score 4 → 90%-100% An imagined situation is established with a narrator and/or characters and a setting. The first sentence captures the reader's interest. Events unfold naturally with a beginning, middle, and end. A strong conclusion from the narrated experience is provided.	Score 4 → 90%-100% The writer's voice creates interest and enjoyment for the reader. The experience is portrayed using dialogue and descriptions that develop experiences and events to show the response of characters to situations. The writer's personality and feelings are expressed in the writing.	Score 4 → 90%-100% Writing shows a strong command of grade level language arts standards. The writer uses correct capitalization, punctuation, and spelling for the most part.	Score 4 → 90%-100% Sentences are varied: simple, compound, and complex. Sentences are well-developed and are interesting to the reader.
Score 3 → 80%-89% An imagined situation is established with a narrator and/or characters and a setting. The first sentence may capture the reader's interest. Events unfold naturally with a beginning, middle, and end. A conclusion from the narrated experience is provided.	Score 3 → 80%-89% The writer's voice creates some interest and enjoyment for the reader. The experience is portrayed using some dialogue and descriptions that develop experiences and events to show the response of characters to situations. Some of the writer's personality and feelings are expressed in the writing.	Score 3 → 80%-89% Writing shows a good command of grade level language arts standards. The few errors in capitalization, punctuation, and spelling do not interfere with understanding.	Score 3 → 80%-89% Sentences are varied for the most part. Sentences are complete and contain details that are interesting to the reader.
Score 2 → 70%-79% An imagined situation is established with a narrator and/or characters and a setting. Writing is somewhat organized, but lacks a complete sequence of events that unfolds naturally. A conclusion is provided.	Score 2 → 70%-79% The writer's voice is usually evident. Writing needs more details. Writing shows some feeling. The writer's personality and feelings are vaguely expressed in the writing.	Score 2 → 70%-79% Writing shows some command of grade level language arts standards. Errors in capitalization, punctuation, and spelling may interfere with understanding.	Score 2 → 70%-79% Sentences are simple with few details. Some sentences are weak or awkward.
Score 1 → Below 70% An imagined situation with characters and a setting may be presented. Writing shows little or no evidence of organization. No conclusion or a weak conclusion is provided.	Score 1 → Below 70% The writer's voice is weak. Few details are provided to interest the reader. The writing is flat. The reader is not engaged.	Score 1 → Below 70% Writing shows little or no command of grade level language arts standards. Errors in capitalization, punctuation, and spelling interfere with understanding.	Score 1 → Below 70% Sentences are often incomplete or confusing.

Argumentative/Persuasive Writing

Argumentative/persuasive writing explains what the author or someone else believes or claims about something. It tries to convince readers to agree with the claim by providing evidence that supports the claim.

Example: Brown bears, specifically the subspecies called grizzly bears, should be reintroduced to the American West. American naturalists from several universities have proof that brown bears once lived throughout the Western United States before rifles were used to hunt them near to extinction. The reintroduction of other endangered animals such as bald eagles and peregrine falcons have been popular with a majority of citizens, so most citizens would be in favor of reintroducing brown bears throughout the Western United States.

5-Step Writing Process

1. **Prewriting - Time to Think**

2. **First Draft - Time to Write**

3. **Revising - Time to Improve Your Writing**

4. **Editing - Time to Make Corrections**

5. **Publishing - Time to Share**

Argumentative/Persuasive Writing Process

Use these steps to write an argumentative/persuasive text.

1. Prewriting - Time to Think
- Brainstorm—discuss your topic with others.
- Consider who will read your writing.
- Gather information about your topic.
- Make a plan stating your claim and the best evidence to support it.

2. First Draft - Time to Write
- Use complete sentences and paragraphs to organize your information.
- Introduce the topic.
- State your claim about the topic. Explain the best evidence to support your claim and provide supporting details for each piece of evidence.
- Write a summary conclusion that briefly restates your claim and evidence you supplied to support it.
- Have others read it and offer suggestions.

3. Revising - Time to Improve Your Writing
- Read what you have written and make changes if needed, keeping in mind what others suggested.
  - Add descriptive words.
  - Add more detail.

4. Editing - Time to Make Corrections
- Make sure you use complete sentences, correct spelling, punctuation, and capitalization.

5. Publishing - Time to Share
- Read it aloud in class.
- Send copies to friends or relatives.

1. Prewriting → Brainstorming

Argumentative/persuasive writing explains what the author or someone else believes or claims about something. It tries to convince readers to agree with the claim by providing evidence that supports the claim.

Phrases to Use When Writing an Argumentative/Persuasive Text

In my opinion	I think	I believe	I have to say that	My point of view
As far as I can see	You can see why	To wrap it up	All things considered
There is no doubt	With this in mind	For example	For instance

 Isaiah was given this writing prompt for an argumentative/persuasive text: Children sometimes disagree with the way something is handled by their parents. Think of something you'd like to change in your household. Write your point of view to try and persuade your parents to make this change.

Isaiah brainstormed and wrote down ideas that he had for a topic for his argumentative/persuasive text. Then he chose one topic.

What will the topic be for my argumentative/persuasive text?	
my own room	take guitar lessons
stay up later	go to the mall with friends
get an allowance	get a dog

Isaiah brainstormed reasons he should receive an allowance to get some ideas on paper before organizing them in the planning step of the writing process.

Get an Allowance	
learn to be responsible	know the cost of products
learn the value of money	make smart decisions
understand where money comes from	work for money
learn to save money to buy things	learn about investing money
donate money	improve math skills

1. Prewriting → Planning

Planning is the process of organizing thoughts and ideas for writing.

 Isaiah used the graphic organizer below to make a plan for his text.

Title

An Allowance

Claim

I should get an allowance.

Evidence

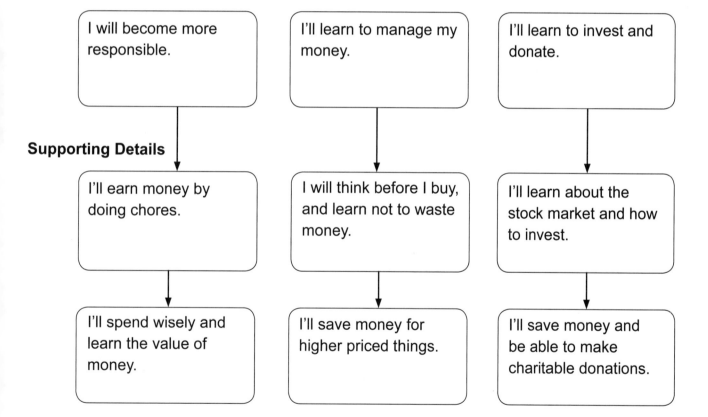

| I will become more responsible. | I'll learn to manage my money. | I'll learn to invest and donate. |

Supporting Details

| I'll earn money by doing chores. | I will think before I buy, and learn not to waste money. | I'll learn about the stock market and how to invest. |

| I'll spend wisely and learn the value of money. | I'll save money for higher priced things. | I'll save money and be able to make charitable donations. |

Conclusion

You can see why getting an allowance would be a valuable experience for me.

2. First Draft

This is Isaiah's argumentative/persuasive text trying to persuade his parents to give him an allowance.

An Allowance

I've wanted to receive an allowance for a long time. Why can't my parents understand why I want an allowance? Most of my friends get an allowance. My parents are great, but when it comes to giving me an allowance, they won't consider it, and I am determined to convince them that an allowance would be good for me.

I believe getting an allowance would help me become a more responsible person. My dad says you shouldn't get payed for doing chores. You should do them because its your responsability. My mom says I can always ask them for money if I want to buy something, but guess what? Lots of times they say no. I have to say that I do my chores. Since my parents think I should not get payed for some chores, maybe I could get a small allowance if I do extra chores. If I complete those chores, I could ask for more chores to earn more money. My parents will get more help around the house with this system. I could mow the lawn or wash the car. I can already smell the freshly cut grass and feel the cool spray of the garden hose. Of course mom, dad, and I will have to have a meeting to decide what the extra chores will be and how much pay I'd get for each chore. We'd probably make a chart to keep track of the chores. The chart will have to be easy to keep up or it won't work.

When I have an allowance, I will have to decide how to spend my money. I think I will be very careful when I'm spending my own money. At least thats what people tell me. Because I'll be making my own decisions on how much money I spend and what I buy, I think I'll learn to spend money wisely. I will think carefully before I buy something. I can look online for sales and coupons. Since my parents always talk about how important it is to be a responsible person, I feel that they will listen to my point of view and consider changing their minds about an allowance.

When I get my allowance, I don't have to spend all of it. I can save money each week, so I'll have it if I want to buy something more expensive. My parents will agree that saving money is a smart thing to do. They tell me that it's not good for kids to get what they want immediately. It's good for them to work for it over time. Mom says, "its important for children to learn to delay gradification." There's no doubt that my parents will be happy to hear me talking about saving money. Mom can put money into a savings account at the bank. I can keep putting change in my big piggybank. I can almost hear the coins clinking as they fall into the piggybank. When my piggybank is full, I can take it to the coin machine at the grocery store. I'll carry the heavy coins into the store and put them in the machine. Then, I'll get dollar bills. Once again, I'll have to decide what to do with my money.

Actually I know what I want to do with the money in the piggybank. I'd like to buy toys with the money and donate them to toys for tots during the holidays. I would also realy like to volunteer to help the workers if they let kids help.

I'd probably have to save for a while, but I want to invest my money someday. I'd like to buy stock in disney. I looked online. You can buy a stock in disney, and you can get a certificate stating that you are a stockholder. The colorful certificates catch your eye with pictures of your favorite disney characters. I could watch how the stock is doing. I would be one of many owners of disney. It would be so exciting to see the stocks go up! Maybe I will make a profit. I'll have to make more decisions about my money.

I truly believe that I will learn a lot about money: spending, saving, donating, and investing. It won't be my parents just giving me money. I will be working in order to earn my allowance. If I don't work, I won't get payed. I'll have to have long term goals when I want to buy something more expensive, when I want to plan ahead to donate toys during the holidays, and when I want to invest some of my money. In my opinion, there is no doubt that my argument in favor of getting an allowance will make sense to my parents.

3. Revising Checklist

Andre read his persuasive writing and circled the answers to the following questions. Then he made revisions to his persuasive text.

1. Does my title make the reader want to read my text?   Yes   No   (Maybe)
    Original Title: An Allowance
    Revised Title: Making Cents

2. Does my first sentence capture the reader's interest?   Yes   No   (Maybe)
    Original First Sentence:
      I've wanted to receive an allowance for a long time.
    Revised:
      I don't always agree with my mom and dad about everything. I guess thats not surprising.

3. Is my text organized with a topic, claim, best evidence for claim, and a summary/conclusion?
                                                                       (Yes)   No   Maybe

4. Does my text make sense?   (Yes)   No   Maybe

5. Do I need to add more details?   (Yes)   No   Maybe

6. Do I need to remove or add any words or sentences?   Yes   No   (Maybe)
    Original First Sentence in the Second Paragraph:
      I believe getting an allowance would help me become a more responsible person.
    Revised:
      First of all I believe getting an allowance would help me become a more responsible person.

    Original First Sentence in the Last Paragraph:
      I truly believe that I will learn a lot about money: spending, saving, donating, and investing.
    Revised:
      As you can see, I truly believe that I will learn a lot about money: spending, saving, donating, and investing.

7. Does the text have my voice, the voice I use when I talk to my family and friends?
                                                                       (Yes)   No   Maybe

8. Do I have my argumentative/persuasive text separated into paragraphs?
                                                                       (Yes)   No   Maybe

9. If there was dialogue did I write it in its own paragraph?   (Yes)   No   Maybe

10. Did I address opposing opinions or viewpoints?   (Yes)   No   Maybe

11. Do I have a summary/conclusion that restates the claim?   (Yes)   No   Maybe

 Isaiah's friend read his argumentative/persuasive text and answered the following questions.

1. Is there anything you would like to know about?
    "Can kids really own stocks?"

Original Sixth Paragraph:
    I'd probably have to save for a while, but I want to invest my money someday. I'd like to buy stock in disney. I looked online. You can buy a stock in disney and you can get a certificate stating that you are a stockholder. The colorful certificates catch your eye with pictures of your favorite Disney characters. I could watch how the stock is doing. I would be one of many owners of Disney. It would be so exciting to see the stocks go up! Maybe I will make a profit. I'll have to make more decisions about my money.

Revised:
    I'd probably have to save for a while, but I want to invest my money someday. I'd like to buy stock in disney. I looked online. You can buy a stock in disney and you can get a certificate stating that you are a stockholder. The colorful certificates catch your eye with pictures of your favorite disney characters. **Mom and Dad would have to do the buying, but it would be my stock. Kids can't buy stocks. I would own the stock, but Mom and Dad would have control of it until I turn eighteen.** I could watch how the stock is doing. I would be one of many owners of disney. It would be so exciting to see the stocks go up! Maybe I will make a profit. I'll have to make more decisions about my money.

2. Is there anything you don't understand?
    "No."

3. Revised Draft

 This is Isaiah's argumentative/persuasive text trying to persuade his parents to give him an allowance.

Making Cents

I don't always agree with my mom and dad about everything. I guess thats not surprising. Why can't my parents understand why I want an allowance? Most of my friends get an allowance. My parents are great, but when it comes to giving me an allowance, they won't consider it, and I am determined to convince them that an allowance would be good for me.

First of all I believe getting an allowance would help me become a more responsable person. My dad says you shouldn't get payed for doing chores. You should do them because its your responsability. My mom says I can always ask them for money if I want to buy something, but guess what? Lots of times they say no. I have to say that I do my chores. Since my parents think I should not get payed for some chores, maybe I could get a small allowance if I do extra chores. If I complete those chores, I could ask for more chores to earn more money. My parents will get more help around the house with this system. I could mow the lawn or wash the car. I can already smell the freshly cut grass and feel the cool spray of the garden hose. Of course mom, dad, and I will have to have a meeting to decide what the extra chores will be and how much pay I'd get for each chore. We'd probably make a chart to keep track of the chores. The chart will have to be easy to keep up or it won't work.

When I have an allowance, I will have to decide how to spend my money. I think I will be very careful when I'm spending my own money. At least thats what people tell me. Because I'll be making my own decisions on how much money I spend and what I buy, I think I'll learn to spend money wisely. I will think carefully before I buy something. I can look online for sales and coupons. Since my parents always talk about how important it is to be a responsable person, I feel that they will listen to my point of view and consider changing their minds about an allowance.

When I get my allowance, I don't have to spend all of it. I can save money each week, so I'll have it if I want to buy something more expensive. My parents will agree that saving money is a smart thing to do. They tell me that it's not good for kids to get what they want immediately. It's good for them to work for it over time. Mom says, "its important for children to learn to delay gradification." There's no doubt that my parents will be happy to hear me talking about saving money. Mom can put money into a savings account at the bank. I can keep putting change in my big piggybank. I can almost hear the coins clinking as they fall into the piggybank. When my piggybank is full, I can take it to the coin machine at the grocery store. I'll carry the heavy coins into the store and put them in the machine. Then, I'll get dollar bills. Once again, I'll have to decide what to do with my money.

Actually I know what I want to do with the money in the piggybank. I'd like to buy toys with the money and donate them to toys for tots during the holidays. I would also realy like to volunteer to help the workers if they let kids help.

I'd probably have to save for a while, but I want to invest my money someday. I'd like to buy stock in disney. I looked online. You can buy a stock in disney, and you can get a certificate stating that you are a stockholder. The colorful certificates catch your eye with pictures of your favorite disney characters. Mom and Dad would have to do the buying, but it would be my stock. Kids can't buy stocks. I would own the stock, but Mom and Dad would have control of it until I turn eighteen. I could watch how the stock is doing. I would be one of many owners of disney. It would be so exciting to see the stocks go up! Maybe I will make a profit. I'll have to make more decisions about my money.

As you can see, I truly believe that I will learn a lot about money: spending, saving, donating, and investing. It won't be my parents just giving me money. I will be working in order to earn my allowance. If I don't work, I won't get payed. I'll have to have long term goals when I want to buy something more expensive, when I want to plan ahead to donate toys during the holidays, and when I want to invest some of my money. In my opinion, there is no doubt that my argument in favor of getting an allowance will make sense to my parents.

4. Editing Checklist

 Isaiah reread and edited his argumentative/persuasive text. He carefully looked for mistakes in spelling, capitalization, punctuation, word usage, and sentence structure.

Spelling

Isaiah checked for spelling errors and used a dictionary to correct the mistakes.

Original: thats	Revised: that's
Original: responsable	Revised: responsible
Original: payed	Revised: paid
Original: responsability	Revised: responsibility
Original: gradification	Revised: gratification
Original: realy	Revised: really

Capitalization

Isaiah checked that he had capitalized:

- The first word of each sentence
- The word I
- Names of people and pets
- Words such as mom, dad, mother, father, aunt, uncle, when they are used as names
  Original: mom, dad, and I
  Revised: **M**om, **D**ad, and **I**

  Original: Mom says, "its important for children to learn to delay gratification."
  Revised: Mom says, "**I**ts important for children to learn to delay gratification."
- Titles when they are used as names
- The first word of a quotation
- Proper Nouns – nouns that name a specific person, place, or thing
  Original: toys for tots
  Revised: **T**oys for **T**ots

  Original: disney
  Revised: **D**isney
- Days of the week and months of the year

Punctuation

Isaiah checked his punctuation: periods, question marks, exclamation points, commas, apostrophes, and quotation marks.

Original: First of all I believe getting an allowance would help me become a more responsible person.

Revised: First of all**,** I believe getting an allowance would help me become a more responsible person.

Original: Of course Mom, Dad, and I will have to have a meeting to decide what the extra chores will be and how much pay I'd get for each chore.

Revised: Of course**,** Mom, Dad, and I will have to have a meeting to decide what the extra chores will be and how much pay I'd get for each chore.

Original: At least that's what people tell me.

Revised: At least**,** that's what people tell me.

Original: Actually I know what I want to do with the money in the piggybank.

Revised: Actually**,** I know what I want to do with the money in the piggybank.

Word Usage

Isaiah read his writing aloud to see if he had used words correctly.

Original: You should do them because **its** your responsibility.

Revised: You should do them because **it's** your responsibility.

Original: Mom says, "Its important for children to learn to delay gratification."

Revised: Mom says, "It's important for children to learn to delay gratification."

Sentence Structure

Isaiah checked to make sure all of his sentences were complete thoughts and that he used simple, compound, and complex sentences. He decided that one sentence was too long. It was rambling.

Original: My parents are great, but when it comes to giving me an allowance, they won't consider it, and I am determined to convince them that an allowance would be good for me.

Revised: My parents are great, but when it comes to giving me an allowance, they won't consider it. I am determined to convince them that an allowance would be good for me.

5. Publishing

This is Isaiah's final copy of his argumentative/persuasive text.

Making Cents

I don't always agree with my mom and dad about everything. I guess that's not surprising. Why can't my parents understand why I want an allowance? Most of my friends get an allowance. My parents are great, but when it comes to giving me an allowance, they won't consider it. I am determined to convince them that an allowance would be good for me.

First of all, I believe getting an allowance would help me become a more responsible person. My dad says you shouldn't get paid for doing chores. You should do them because it's your responsibility. My mom says I can always ask them for money if I want to buy something, but guess what? Lots of times they say no. I have to say that I do my chores. Since my parents think I should not get paid for some chores, maybe I could get a small allowance if I do extra chores. If I complete those chores, I could ask for more chores to earn more money. My parents will get more help around the house with this system. I could mow the lawn or wash the car. I can already smell the freshly cut grass and feel the cool spray of the garden hose. Of course, Mom, Dad, and I will have to have a meeting to decide what the extra chores will be and how much pay I'd get for each chore. We'd probably make a chart to keep track of the chores. The chart will have to be easy to keep up or it won't work.

When I have an allowance, I will have to decide how to spend my money. I think I will be very careful when I'm spending my own money. At least, that's what people tell me. Because I'll be making my own decisions on how much money I spend and what I buy, I think I'll learn to spend money wisely. I will think carefully before I buy something. I can look online for sales and coupons. Since my parents always talk about how important it is to be a responsible person, I feel that they will listen to my point of view and consider changing their minds about an allowance.

When I get my allowance, I don't have to spend all of it. I can save money each week, so I'll have it if I want to buy something more expensive. My parents will agree that saving money is a smart thing to do. They tell me that it's not good for kids to get what they want immediately. It's good for them to work for it over time. Mom says, "It's important for children to learn to delay gratification." There's no doubt that my parents will be happy to hear me talking about saving money. Mom can put money into a savings account at the bank. I can keep putting change in my big piggybank. I can almost hear the coins clinking as they fall into the piggybank. When my piggybank is full, I can take it to the coin machine at the grocery store. I'll carry the heavy coins into the store and put them in the machine. Then, I'll get dollar bills. Once again, I'll have to decide what to do with my money.

Actually, I know what I want to do with the money in the piggybank. I'd like to buy toys with the money and donate them to Toys for Tots during the holidays. I would also really like to volunteer to help the workers if they let kids help.

I'd probably have to save for a while, but I also want to invest my money someday. I'd like to buy stock in Disney. I looked online. You can buy a stock in Disney, and you can get a certificate stating that you are a stockholder. The colorful certificates catch your eye with pictures of your favorite Disney characters. Mom and Dad would have to do the buying, but it would be my stock. I could watch how the stock is doing. I would be one of many owners of Disney. It would be so exciting to see the stocks go up! Maybe I will make a profit. I'll have to make more decisions about my money.

As you can see, I truly believe that I will learn a lot about money: spending, saving, donating, and investing. It won't be my parents just giving me money. I will be working in order to earn my allowance. If I don't work, I won't get paid. I'll have to have long term goals when I want to buy something more expensive, when I want to plan ahead to donate toys during the holidays, and when I want to invest some of my money. In my opinion, there is no doubt that my argument in favor of getting an allowance will make sense to my parents.

1. Prewriting → Brainstorming

Argumentative/persuasive writing explains what the author or someone else believes or claims about something. It tries to convince readers to agree with the claim by providing evidence that supports the claim.

Phrases to Use When Writing an Argumentative/Persuasive Text

In my opinion	I think I believe	I have to say that	My point of view
As far as I can see	You can see why	To wrap it up	All things considered
There is no doubt	With this in mind	For example	For instance

Write an argumentative/persuasive text to convince your parents to change something in your household or choose a writing prompt on page 71. Refer to the Writing Process on pages 48 and 49 for information about writing an argumentative/persuasive text. For an example see pages 50-61.

Brainstorm ideas for a topic for your argumentative/persuasive text. Then circle the topic you have chosen.

What will the topic be for my argumentative/persuasive text?

Write the topic you chose on the blank line below. Brainstorm ideas you have about your topic and write them below your topic.

_____

1. Prewriting → Planning

Planning is the process of organizing thoughts and ideas for writing.

Use the graphic organizer below to make a plan for writing your argumentative/persuasive text.

Title

Claim

Evidence

Supporting Details

Conclusion

2. First Draft

Use your plans to help you write the first draft of your argumentative/persuasive text.

_____

_____

_____

_____

_____

_____

_____

_____

_____

_____

_____

_____

_____

_____

_____

_____

3. Revising Checklist

Authors revise the text to make their writing better.

Reread the first draft of your argumentative/persuasive text. Ask yourself the following questions and circle your answers. Use the information you gather from these questions to revise your writing. Write changes on your first draft using arrows (^) to show where to add words or sentences. Draw a line through words or sentences you've decided to remove.

Niagara Falls

^ It was gigantic

1. Does my title make the reader want to read my text?   Yes   No   Maybe

   Notes: _____

   _____

2. Does my first sentence capture the reader's interest?   Yes   No   Maybe

   Notes: _____

   _____

3. Is my text organized with a topic, claim, best evidence for claim, and a summary/conclusion?
                                                                        Yes   No   Maybe

   Notes: _____

   _____

4. Does my text make sense?   Yes   No   Maybe

   Notes: _____

   _____

5. Do I need to add more details?   Yes   No   Maybe

    Notes: _____

    _____

6. Do I need to remove or add any words or sentences?   Yes   No   Maybe

    Notes: _____

    _____

7. Does the text have my voice, the voice I use when I talk to my family and friends?
                                                                      Yes   No   Maybe

    Notes: _____

    _____

8. Do I have my argumentative/persuasive text separated into paragraphs?
                                                                      Yes   No   Maybe

    Notes: _____

    _____

9. Did I write dialogue in its own paragraph?   Yes   No   Maybe

    Notes: _____

    _____

10. Did I address opposing opinions or viewpoints?   Yes   No   Maybe

    Notes: _____

    _____

11. Do I have a summary/conclusion that restates the claim?   Yes   No   Maybe

Notes: _____

_____

Ask a friend or a family member to read your writing and answer the following questions. Write the answers below the questions.

1. Is there anything you'd like to know more about?

Notes: _____

_____

_____

2. Is there anything you don't understand?

Notes: _____

_____

_____

3. Revised Draft

Use your notes to revise the first draft of your argumentative/persuasive text.

_____

_____

_____

_____

_____

_____

_____

_____

_____

_____

_____

_____

_____

_____

_____

_____

_____

4. Editing Checklist

Reread and edit the revised draft of your argumentative/persuasive text. Look carefully for mistakes in spelling, capitalization, punctuation, word usage, and sentence structure.

Spelling

Check for spelling errors. Use a dictionary to help correct spelling errors.

Circle words that are misspelled and write the correct spelling above.

Capitalization

Check to make sure you've capitalized:

- The first word of each sentence
- The word I
- Names of people and pets
- Words like mom, dad, mother, father, aunt, uncle when they are used as names
- Titles when they are used with names
- The first word of a quotation
- Proper nouns–nouns that name a specific person, place, or thing
- Days of week and months of the year

Underline any letters that need to be capitalized.

Punctuation

Check your punctuation: periods, question marks, exclamation points, commas, apostrophes, and quotation marks.

Use an arrow (∧) with the correct punctuation mark above to show where it needs to be inserted.

Word Usage

Read your writing aloud to see if you've used words correctly.

Put a line through words used incorrectly and write the correction above.

Sentence Structure

Check to make sure all of your sentences are complete thoughts. If all of your sentences are simple sentences, try to make some compound or complex.

Put lines through words you do not want to use. Use arrows (∧) to show where words should be added.

5. Publishing

Write the final copy of your argumentative/persuasive text with the changes from your editing and revising.

_____

_____

_____

_____

_____

_____

_____

_____

_____

_____

_____

_____

_____

_____

_____

Argumentative/Persuasive Writing Prompts

1. Write about how you feel about many public schools requiring students to wear uniforms.

2. Some people believe that the A, B, C, D, F grading system should be replaced with the Pass/Fail system. What is your claim?

3. Families come in many sizes. Some families have one or two children. Others have three or more. Are large families better than small families?

4. We all have activities we enjoy. Write to convince readers to try an activity that you value and enjoy.

5. Do you think technology has led to people having less human contact? Explain/support your claim.

6. What do you think is the most important invention in the past hundred years? Why is it more important than other inventions?

7. Write a letter to your parents persuading them to give you permission to do something.

8. Some people believe that everyone on a team should get a trophy for participating. Others believe that trophies should be given for accomplishments such as best player, most improved player, and player with great sportsmanship. What is your opinion/argument and why?

9. Do you think you should be allowed to have a television in your room?

10. Would you rather live in an urban, suburban, or rural area?

11. Some people think that school should be year round with short vacations throughout the year. Write to express and support your argument.

12. Many people think that a pet is a valuable addition to a family. Argue your claim.

13. Should people be allowed to bring their pets to school and work?

14. Some people believe that participating in team sports helps build character. What is your claim?

15. Are people too dependent on technology? Explain using evidence.

Argumentative/Persuasive Writing Rubric

Organization	Voice and Word Choice	Language Arts Standards	Sentence Structure
Score 4 → 90-100 The writer states his or her claim in the introduction. The first sentence captures the reader's interest. The writer gives evidence that supports the claim. Opposing viewpoints are addressed. A strong conclusion supporting the claim is provided.	**Score 4 → 90%-100%** The writer's voice creates interest and enjoyment for the reader. The writer expresses his or her opinion clearly and effectively. The reader can tell how strongly the writer feels about his or her opinion. The writer's personality and feelings are expressed in the writing.	**Score 4 → 90%-100%** Writing shows a strong command of grade level language arts standards. The writer uses correct capitalization, punctuation, and spelling for the most part.	**Score 4 → 90%-100%** Sentences are varied: simple, compound, and complex. Sentences are well-developed and are interesting to the reader.
Score 3 → 80-89 The writer states his or her claim in the introduction. The first sentence may capture the reader's interest. The writer gives evidence that supports the claim. A conclusion supporting the claim is provided.	**Score 3 → 80%-89%** The writer's voice creates some interest and enjoyment for the reader. The opinion is expressed clearly. The writing is lacking a bit in elaboration. Some of the writer's personality and feelings are expressed in the writing.	**Score 3 → 80%-89%** Writing shows a good command of grade level language arts standards. The few errors in capitalization, punctuation, and spelling do not interfere with understanding.	**Score 3 → 80%-89%** Sentences are varied for the most part. Sentences are complete and contain details that are interesting to the reader.
Score 2 → 70-79 The writer states his or her claim in the introduction. The first sentence may capture the reader's interest. The writing may be somewhat organized, but lacks evidence. A conclusion that may support the claim is provided.	**Score 2 → 70%-79%** The writer's voice is usually evident. Writing needs more details and organization. Writing shows some feeling. The writer's personality and feelings are vaguely expressed in the writing.	**Score 2 → 70%-79%** Writing shows some command of grade level language arts standards. Errors in capitalization, punctuation, and spelling may interfere with understanding.	**Score 2 → 70%-79%** Sentences are simple with few details. Some sentences are weak or awkward.
Score 1 → Below 70 The writer states his or her claim. Writing shows little or no evidence of organization. Very little or no evidence is given. No conclusion or a weak conclusion is provided.	**Score 1 → Below 70%** The writer's voice is weak. Few details are provided to interest the reader. The writing is flat. The reader is not engaged.	**Score 1 → Below 70%** Writing shows little or no command of grade level language arts standards. Errors in capitalization, punctuation, and spelling interfere with understanding.	**Score 1 → Below 70%** Sentences are often incomplete or confusing.

Informative/Explanatory Writing

Informative/explanatory writing gives readers information/facts about a topic. The author must research the topic using sources such as books, articles, and the Internet. The author may use illustrations and diagrams to help the reader understand the topic or just to add interest.

Example: To have great tomatoes in your garden, it is best to start early. Place two or three seeds into small containers or each cell of a seed starter. Cover the seeds with 1/4 inch of soil and gently tamp it over the seeds. Water to ensure good seed-to-soil contact. Place the containers in a warm, sunny spot. Cover with a clear plastic top or plastic wrap. Keep the soil moist. When the plants are a couple of inches tall, transfer each to larger, individual pots. Once the weather warms, plant the tomatoes in your garden.

5-Step Writing Process

1. **Prewriting - Time to Think**

2. **First Draft - Time to Write**

3. **Revising - Time to Improve Your Writing**

4. **Editing - Time to Make Corrections**

5. **Publishing - Time to Share**

Informative/Explanatory Writing Process

Use these steps to write an informative/explanatory essay.

1. Prewriting - Time to Think
- Brainstorm ideas for your topic.
- Make a plan organizing information in a logical sequence.

2. First Draft - Time to Write
- Introductory sentence should capture the interest of the reader.
- Use you planning to organize your text in a logical sequence.
- Provide a conclusion.
- Have others read it and offer suggestions.

3. Revising - Time to Improve Your Writing
- Read what you have written and make changes if needed, keeping in mind what others suggested.
  - Make sure your text is presented in an organized way.

4. Editing - Time to Make Corrections
- Make sure you use complete sentences, correct spelling, punctuation, and capitalization.

5. Publishing - Time to Share
- Read it aloud in class.
- Send copies to friends or relatives.

1. Prewriting → Brainstorming

Informative/explanatory writing gives readers information/facts about a topic. The author must research the topic using sources such as books, articles, and the Internet. The author may use illustrations and diagrams to help the reader understand the topic or just to add interest.

An author may not copy information that is found word for word. Notes should be taken when the information is read. The author should make sure he/she understands the information and then change the wording to his/her own words. This is called *paraphrasing*. The sources used should be referenced (cited).

Printed Source Citation

Author Last Name, First Name. *Book Title*. Publisher, date published.
Wade, Mary Dodson. *Amazing Civil War Nurse Clara Barton*. Enslow Publishers, 2010.

Web Source Citation

Author Last, First Name. "Title of Publication". *Website Name*. URL. Date accessed.
"Barton, Clara". *World Book Online*. www.worldbookonline.com/kids. 21 June 2016.

 Chloe's assignment for her informative/explanatory essay was to compare and contrast two historical figures.

Chloe brainstormed and wrote down ideas that she had for a topic for her informative/explanatory writing. Then she chose one topic.

Which historical figures will be the topic for my informative/explanatory essay?	
John Wilkes Boothe and Lee Harvey Oswald	Woodrow Wilson and Franklin D. Roosevelt
Sally Ride and Christa McCauliffe	Thomas Edison and Alexander Graham Bell
⟨Louis Braille and Helen Keller⟩	Harriet Tubman and Martin Luther King Jr.

Chloe brainstormed about Louis Braille and Helen Keller to get some ideas on paper before organizing them in the planning step of the writing process.

Louis Braille and Helen Keller	
Alike	**Different**
Louis and Helen were blind.	Helen also could not hear.
They both learned to communicate.	Helen communicated with people by feeling sign language with her hand.
Even with their disabilities, Louis and Helen worked hard to learn.	Louis developed a system blind people could use to read.
They both had teachers who helped them.	Helen used Louis Braille's system to read.
Louis and Helen helped other people to overcome their disabilities.	Helen wrote her autobiography.

1. Prewriting → Planning

Planning is the process of organizing thoughts and ideas for writing.

 Chloe decided to use a Venn diagram to make a plan for her informative/explanatory essay. A Venn diagram is a graphic organizer used to compare and contrast two objects, events, people, or concepts. The Venn diagram helps writers understand how two things can be alike and different at the same time.

Louis Braille

- born in France in 1809
- cut his eye at age 3
- eye got infected
- infection led to blindness
- focused on sound, smell, and touch
- his father hammered nails on a board and taught Louis the alphabet and how to form words
- attended school and was an excellent student
- sent to the National Institute for Blind Children in Paris, the first school for the blind
- learned sonography at age twelve
- used sonography to invent braille
- helped blind people his whole life

Both

- born with eyesight
- blinded at a very young age
- learned to communicate
- worked hard to get an education
- had special teachers who were important in their lives
- helped other people throughout their lives

Helen Keller

- born in U.S. in 1880
- at 19 months old became ill
- became deaf and blind
- was frustrated and became mischievous
- was referred to teacher, Anne Sullivan, by Perkins School for the Blind
- learned when Anne spelled words in the palm of Helen's hand
- learned manners and good behavior
- went to college and graduated
- wrote *The Story of My Life*
- worked to help others, especially blind people
- worked for the American Foundation of the Blind
- visited injured soldiers in hospitals during World War II
- gave soldiers hope

2. First Draft

This is Chloe's informative/explanatory essay comparing and contrasting Louis Braille and Helen Keller.

Louis and Helen

Louis Braille and Helen Keller didn't know each other. Louis and Helen didn't live at the same time. Louis was born in 1809 in France, and he died in 1852. Helen was born in 1880 in the United States. Louis knew nothing about Helen. She was born after he died. However, Helen Keller knew about Louis Braille. Louis and Helen did have something in common. At a very young age, both Louis and Helen suffered physical alments that led to blindness.

At the age of three, Louis Braille wandered into his father's workshop when his father was busy talking to a customer, and picked up a sharp tool. As he played with the tool, it slipped and cut his eye. Mr. and Mrs. Braille took Louis to an old woman who was known as a healer. She put lily water on the wound. Then, the Brailles took Louis to see a doctor. Nothing could be done to save the eye. It became infected, and the infection spread to his other eye. A short time later, Louis lost his eyesight.

Helen Keller began to talk at a young age, six months old. A year later, she became sick with a high fever. Helen's mother took care of her. She cooled the fever with wet towels. Soon the illness was gone. Helen seemed different. Bright lights made her turn her head. She didn't hear when people spoke to her. Helen was blind and deaf. She struggled in a world of silence and darkness.

Louis had to learn how to live in the world as a blind person. He had to learn to walk without bumping into things. Louis used a cane to feel the space in front of him to see if it was clear to walk. Since Louis could not see, he relied on sounds and smells to make sense of the world. He could tell who was coming by the sound of their footsteps. When Louis was a young boy, his father pounded nails into a board to form letters. By touching the top of the nails, he learned the letters of the alphabet. Then, his father taught him to put the letters together to make words.

Helen forgot the words she knew when she was a baby. She couldn't re-learn to talk, because she didn't hear other people talking. Helen used her hands to try and show people what she wanted. Since Helen could not always let people know what she wanted, she was often frustrated and angry. She hit bit and kicked people. Helen's parents let her run wild, because they felt sorry for her. Helen even took food from other peoples plates at meals. Helen's parents took her to see Alexander Graham Bell, the first person to patent the telephone. At one time, Dr. Bell had taught at a school for the deaf. He adviced Helen's parents to write to the Perkins Institute for the Blind. The director of the school sent Anne Sullivan a resent graduate to teach Helen. Anne first taught Helen the proper way to behave. Then, she began to teach Helen sign language.

Louis attended school. His teacher thought he was a good student, but Louis could only learn by listening. He couldn't read the books the other students read. When Louis was ten, he went to Paris to the National Institute for Blind Children, the world's first school for the blind. At this school, there were books Louis could read. The books had raized letters Louis could touch. The letters were huge and the books were heavy. Feeling each letter with his fingers took a long time, but at least Louis was reading. Later, Louis was taught sonography, a code of raized dots and dashes. It was invented by a captain in the french army so soldiers could read messages in the dark. Sonography was also known as night writing. The soldiers could read the messages by touching. Louis used sonography to read and write, but it took many dots to write even one word. Louis got an idea. He decided to write his own code. He worked on it late at night when everyone was sleeping and early in the morning before school.

Anne Sullivan used a finger alphabet to teach Helen words. She had Helen hold a doll. Anne spelled d-o-l-l in the palm of Helen's other hand, but Helen did not understand. Anne tried and tried, but Helen didn't understand that the sign language represented letters and words. Then, one day Helen's world changed. Anne and Helen stood at an outdoor water pump. Anne was filling a pail with water. She took Helen's hand and put it under the water and spelled w-a-t-e-r in Helen's other hand. Helen understood that water was the name of what she was feeling. She realized that everything had a name. Helen began touching things such as a tree a stone and a fence. She wanted Anne to spell the names of everything.

Louis went to the school principal and showed him his system. The new system used raized dots and was a lot easier to learn and read than sonography. At first, Braille's new system was not excepted, but the students at the National Institute recognized how braille was much easier to use than the old system. Many people thought it would be too expensive. Louis and his friend made the first braille writing board. Finally, Louis and other blind people would be able to write. Eventually, Louis Braille became a teacher at the National Institute for the Blind. Louis was a patient kind and gentle teacher.

Helen learned thousands of words. Then, Anne Sullivan taught Helen to read using braille, the raized dot system invented by Louis Braille. Helen also learned to speak. Her speech was hard to understand, because she couldn't hear what she was saying. In 1900, Helen started college. Helen graduated with honors from Radcliffe College. During her college years, Helen wrote *The Story of My Life*. Helen wrote more books and articles about her life and how Anne Sullivan helped her to make sense of the world. Anne died in 1936 after being with Helen for almost fifty years. Helen helped others, especially the blind. During world war II, Helen visited soldiers in hospitals. Meeting Helen gave them hope and encouragement.

Louis Braille and Helen Keller faced many challenges throughout life. Both of them lost their eyesight at a young age. Each of them worked very hard to learn to communicate in spite of their disabilities. Helen and Louis were good students eager to learn. They worked hard to get an education. Both Louis and Helen were fortunate to have excellent teachers in their lives. Though their hard work and determination, Helen Keller and Louis Braille helped many people overcome their disabilities. Even through they died a long time ago, Helen and Louis continue to give hope and guidance to a great number of people.

3. Revising Checklist

 Chloe read her informative/explanatory essay and circled the answers to the following questions. Then she made revisions to her essay.

1. Does my title make the reader want to read my essay?   Yes   No   (Maybe)
    Original Title: Louis and Helen
    Revised Title: Touching Words

2. Does my first sentence capture the reader's interest?   Yes   (No)   Maybe
    Original First Sentence:
        Louis Braille and Helen Keller didn't know each other.
    Revised:
        Louis Braille never met Helen Keller, but he made a great difference in her life.

3. Is my writing organized with a beginning, a middle, and an end?   (Yes)   No   Maybe

4. Did I start a new paragraph for each idea/point?   (Yes)   No   Maybe

5. Does my essay make sense?   (Yes)   No   Maybe

6. Did I paraphrase when gathering information?   (Yes)   No   Maybe

7. Do I need to add more details?   (Yes)   No   Maybe
    Original Ninth Paragraph:
        Helen learned thousands of words. Then, Anne Sullivan taught Helen to read using Braille, the raized dot system invented by Louis Braille. Helen also learned to speak. Her speech was hard to understand, because she couldn't hear what she was saying. In 1900, Helen started college. Helen graduated with honors from Radcliffe College. During her college years, Helen wrote *The Story of My Life*. Helen wrote more books and articles about her life and how Anne Sullivan helped her to make sense of the world. Anne died in 1936 after being with Helen for almost fifty years. Helen helped others, especially the blind. During world war II, Helen visited soldiers in hospitals. Meeting Helen gave them hope and encouragement.

    Revised:
        Helen learned thousands of words. Then, Anne Sullivan taught Helen to read using braille, the raized dot system invented by Louis Braille. Helen also learned to speak. Her speech was hard to understand, because she couldn't hear what she was saying. In 1900, Helen started college. **Anne sat next to her and spelled into Helen's hand all that was said.** Helen graduated with honors from Radcliffe College. During her college years, Helen wrote *The Story of My Life*. Helen wrote more books and articles about her life and how

Anne Sullivan helped her to make sense of the world. Anne died in 1936 after being with Helen for almost fifty years. Helen helped others, especially the blind. During world war II, Helen visited soldiers in hospitals. Meeting Helen gave them hope and encouragement.

8. Do I need to remove or add any words or sentences?   Yes   No   (Maybe)

9. Do I have a conclusion paragraph?   (Yes)   No   Maybe

10. Did I cite sources?   Yes   (No)   Maybe
       Revised:

References

Stuckey, Kenneth A. "Keller, Helen," *World Book Student.* www.worldbookonline.com/kids. 28 Feb. 2017.

Stuckey, Kenneth A. "Braille, Louis," *World Book Student.* www.worldbookonline.com/kids. 28 Feb. 2017.

Kent, Deborah. *Helen Keller: Author and Advocate for the Disabled.* The Child's World, 2004

Freedman, Russell. *Out of the Darkness: The Story Of Louis Braille.* Clarion Books, 1997.

Ask a friend or family member to read your informative/explanatory essay and answer the following questions.

 Chloe's friend read her informative/explanatory essay and answered the following questions.

1. Is there anything you'd like to know more about?

    "What kind of workshop did Louis Braille's father have?

    Louis cut himself with a tool. What kind of tool was it?

    Also, I'd like see braille and sign language.

    How did Helen feel about Louis?"

Original Second Paragraph:
    At the age of three, Louis Braille wandered into his father's workshop when his father was busy talking to a customer and Louis picked up a sharp tool. As he played with the tool, it slipped and cut his eye. Mr. and Mrs. Braille took Louis to an old woman who was thought of as a healer. She put lily water on the wound. Then, the Brailles took Louis to see a doctor. Nothing could be done to save the eye. It became infected, and the infection spread to his other eye. A short time later, Louis lost his eyesight.

Revised:
    Louis Braille loved to watch his father work making saddles and harnesses. He was fascinated by the tools his father used. At the age of three, Louis Braille wandered into his father's workshop when his father was busy talking to a customer and Louis picked up a sharp tool called an awl. As he played with the tool, it slipped

and cut his eye. Mr. and Mrs. Braille took Louis to an old woman who was thought of as a healer. She put lily water on the wound. Then, the Brailles took Louis to see a doctor. Nothing could be done to save the eye. It became infected, and the infection spread to his other eye. A short time later, Louis lost his eyesight.

Chloe decided to add the following text features.

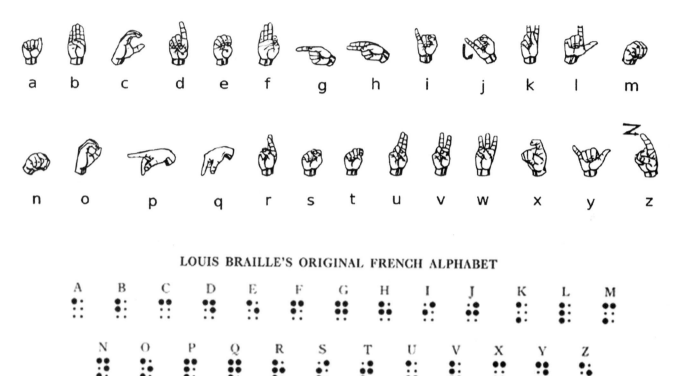

"In our way, we, the blind, are as indebted to Louis Braille as mankind is to Gutenberg."

- Helen Keller

Note: Johannes Gutenberg changed history with his invention of the printing press. Books no longer had to be handwritten. Everyone would have access to books in libraries.

2. Is there anything you don't understand?
    "No."

3. Revised Draft

 This is Chloe's revision of her informative/explanatory essay comparing and contrasting Louis Braille and Helen Keller.

Touching Words

Louis Braille never met Helen Keller, but he made a great difference in her life. Louis and Helen didn't live at the same time. Louis was born in 1809 in France, and he died in 1852. Helen was born in 1880 in the United States. Louis knew nothing about Helen. She was born after he died. However, Helen Keller knew about Louis Braille. Louis and Helen did have something in common. At a very young age, both Louis and Helen suffered physical alments that led to blindness.

Louis Braille loved to watch his father work making saddles and harnesses. He was fascinated by the tools his father used. At the age of three, Louis Braille wandered into his father's workshop when his father was busy talking to a customer and picked up a sharp tool called an awl. As he played with the tool, it slipped and cut his eye. Mr. and Mrs. Braille took Louis to an old woman who was known as a healer. She put lily water on the wound. Then, the Brailles took Louis to see a doctor. Nothing could be done to save the eye. It became infected, and the infection spread to his other eye. A short time later, Louis lost his eyesight.

Helen Keller began to talk at a young age, six months old. A year later, she became sick with a high fever. Helen's mother took care of her. She cooled the fever with wet towels. Soon the illness was gone. Helen seemed different. Bright lights made her turn her head. She didn't hear when people spoke to her. Helen was blind and deaf. She struggled in a world of silence and darkness.

Louis had to learn how to live in the world as a blind person. He had to learn to walk without bumping into things. Louis used a cane to feel the space in front of him to see if it was clear to walk. Since Louis could not see, he relied on sounds and smells to make sense of the world. He could tell who was coming by the sound of their footsteps. When Louis was a young boy, his father pounded nails into a board to form letters. By touching the top of the nails, he learned the letters of the alphabet. Then, his father taught him to put the letters together to make words.

Helen forgot the words she knew when she was a baby. She couldn't re-learn to talk, because she didn't hear other people talking. Helen used her hands to try and show people what she wanted. Since Helen could not always let people know what she wanted, she was often frustrated and angry. She hit bit and kicked people. Helen's parents let her run wild, because they felt sorry for her. Helen even took food from other peoples plates at meals. Helen's parents took her to see Alexander Graham Bell, the first person to patent the telephone. At one time, Dr. Bell had taught at a school for the deaf. He adviced Helen's parents to write to the Perkins Institute for the Blind. The director of the school sent Anne Sullivan a resent graduate to teach Helen. Anne first taught Helen the proper way to behave. Then, she began to teach Helen sign language.

Louis attended school. His teacher thought he was a good student, but Louis could only learn by listening. He couldn't read the books the other students read. When Louis was ten, he went to Paris to the National Institute for Blind Children, the world's first school for the blind. At this school, there were books Louis could read. The books had raized letters Louis could touch. The letters were huge and the books were heavy. Feeling each letter with his fingers took a long time, but at least Louis was reading. Later, Louis was taught sonography, a code of raized dots and dashes. It was invented by a captain in the french army so soldiers could read messages in the dark. Sonography was also known as night writing. The soldiers could read the messages by touching. Louis used sonography to read and write, but it took many dots to write even one word. Louis got an idea. He decided to write his own code. He worked on it late at night when everyone was sleeping and early in the morning before school.

Anne Sullivan used a finger alphabet to teach Helen words. She had Helen hold a doll. Anne spelled d-o-l-l in the palm of Helen's other hand, but Helen did not understand. Anne tried and tried, but Helen didn't understand that the sign language represented letters and words. Then, one day Helen's world changed. Anne and Helen stood at an outdoor water pump. Anne was filling a pail with water. She took Helen's hand and put it under the water and spelled w-a-t-e-r in Helen's other hand. Helen understood that water was the name of what she was feeling. She realized that everything had a name. Helen began touching things such as a tree a stone and a fence. She wanted Anne to spell the names of everything.

AMERICAN SIGN LANGUAGE ALPHABET

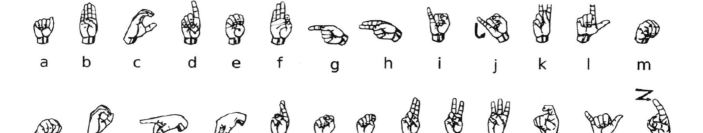

Louis went to the school principal and showed him his system. The new system used raized dots and was a lot easier to learn and read than sonography. At first, Braille's new system was not excepted, but the students at the National Institute recognized how braille was much easier to use than the old system. Many people thought it would be too expensive. Louis and his friend made the first braille writing board. Finally, Louis and other blind people would be able to write. Eventually, Louis Braille became a teacher at the National Institute for the Blind. Louis was a patient kind and gentle teacher.

LOUIS BRAILLE'S ORIGINAL FRENCH ALPHABET

A   B   C   D   E   F   G   H   I   J   K   L   M

N   O   P   Q   R   S   T   U   V   X   Y   Z

Helen learned thousands of words. Then, Anne Sullivan taught Helen to read using braille, the raized dot system invented by Louis Braille. Helen also learned to speak. Her speech was hard to understand, because she couldn't hear what she was saying. In 1900, Helen started college. Anne sat next to her and spelled into Helen's hand all that was said. Helen graduated with honors from Radcliffe College. During her college years, Helen wrote *The Story of My Life*. Helen wrote more books and articles about her life and how Anne Sullivan helped her to make sense of the world. Anne died in 1936 after being with Helen for almost fifty years. Helen helped others, especially the blind. During world war II, Helen visited soldiers in hospitals. Meeting Helen gave them hope and encouragement.

Louis Braille and Helen Keller faced many challenges throughout life. Both of them lost their eyesight at a young age. Each of them worked very hard to learn to communicate in spite of their disabilities. Helen and Louis were good students eager to learn. They worked hard to get an education. Both Louis and Helen were fortunate to have excellent teachers in their lives. Though their hard work and determination, Helen Keller and Louis Braille helped many people overcome their disabilities. Even though they died a long time ago, Helen and Louis continue to give hope and guidance to a great number of people.

"In our way, we, the blind, are as indebted to Louis Braille as mankind is to Gutenberg."
- Helen Keller

Note: Johannes Gutenberg changed history with his invention of the printing press. Books did not have to be handwritten. Everyone would have access to books in libraries.

References

Stuckey, Kenneth A. "Keller, Helen". *World Book Online*. www.worldbookonline.com/kids. 28 Feb. 2017.
Stuckey, Kenneth A. "Braille, Louis". *World Book Online*. www.worldbookonline.com/kids. 28 Feb. 2017.
Kent, Deborah. *Helen Keller: Author and Advocate for the Disabled*. The Child's World, 2004.
Freedman, Russell. *Out of the Darkness: The Story Of Louis Braille*. Clarion Books, 1997.

4. Editing Checklist

 Chloe reread her writing and edited her informative/explanatory essay. She looked carefully for mistakes in spelling, capitalization, punctuation, word usage, and sentence structure.

Spelling

Chloe checked for spelling errors and used a dictionary to correct them.

Original: alments	Revised: ailments
Original: resent	Revised: recent
Original: raized	Revised: raised

Capitalization

Chloe checked to see if she capitalized:

- The first word of each sentence
- The word I
- Names of people and pets
- Words like mom, dad, mother, father, aunt, uncle when they are used as names
- Titles when they are used with names
- The first word of a quotation
- Proper nouns- nouns that name a specific person, place, or thing

    Original: french   Revised: **F**rench
    Original: world war II   Revised: **W**orld **W**ar II

- Days of the week and months of the year

Punctuation

Chloe checked her punctuation: periods, question marks, exclamation points, commas, apostrophes, and quotation marks.

Original: She hit bit and kicked people.   Revised: She hit**,** bit**,** and kicked people.
Original: peoples   Revised: people's

Original: The director of the school sent Anne Sullivan a recent graduate to teach Helen.
Revised: The director of the school sent Anne Sullivan**,** a recent graduate**,** to teach Helen.

Original: The letters were huge and the books were heavy.
Revised: The letters were huge**,** and the books were heavy.

Original: Helen began touching things such as a tree a stone and a fence.
Revised: Helen began touching things such as a tree, a stone, and a fence.

Original: Louis was a patient kind and gentle teacher.
Revised: Louis was a patient, kind, and gentle teacher.

Sentence Structure

Original: At the age of three, Louis Braille wandered into his father's workshop when his father was busy talking to a customer and Louis picked up a sharp tool called an awl.
Revised: At the age of three, Louis Braille wandered into his father's workshop when his father was busy talking to a customer. Louis picked up a sharp tool called an awl.

Original: Soon the illness was gone. Helen seemed different.
Revised: Soon the illness was gone, but Helen seemed different.

Word Usage

Chloe read her essay aloud to see if she had used her words correctly.

Original: adviced	Revised: advised
Original: excepted	Revised: accepted
Original: though	Revised: through

5. Publishing

 This is Chloe's final copy of her informative/explanatory essay comparing and contrasting Louis Braille and Helen Keller.

Touching Words

Louis Braille never met Helen Keller, but he made a great difference in her life. Louis and Helen didn't live at the same time. Louis was born in 1809 in France, and he died in 1852. Helen was born in 1880 in the United States. Louis knew nothing about Helen. She was born after he died. However, Helen Keller knew about Louis Braille. Louis and Helen did have something in common. At a very young age, both Louis and Helen suffered physical ailments that led to blindness.

Louis Braille loved to watch his father work making saddles and harnesses. He was fascinated by the tools his father used. At the age of three, Louis Braille wandered into his father's workshop when his father was busy talking to a customer. Louis picked up a sharp tool called an awl. As he played with the tool, it slipped and cut his eye. Mr. and Mrs. Braille took Louis to an old woman who was known as a healer. She put lily water on the wound. Then, the Brailles took Louis to see a doctor. Nothing could be done to save the eye. It became infected, and the infection spread to his other eye. A short time later, Louis lost his eyesight.

Helen Keller began to talk at a young age, six months old. A year later, she became sick with a high fever. Helen's mother took care of her. She cooled the fever with wet towels. Soon the illness was gone, but Helen seemed different. Bright lights made her turn her head. She didn't hear when people spoke to her. Helen was blind and deaf. She struggled in a world of silence and darkness.

Louis had to learn how to live in the world as a blind person. He had to learn to walk without bumping into things. Louis used a cane to feel the space in front of him to see if it was clear to walk. Since Louis could not see, he relied on sounds and smells to make sense of the world. He could tell who was coming by the sound of their footsteps. When Louis was a young boy, his father pounded nails into a board to form letters. By touching the top of the nails, he learned the letters of the alphabet. Then, his father taught him to put the letters together to make words.

Helen forgot the words she knew when she was a baby. She couldn't re-learn to talk, because she didn't hear other people talking. Helen used her hands to try and show people what she wanted. Since Helen could not always let people know what she wanted, she was often frustrated and angry. She hit, bit, and kicked people. Helen's parents let her run wild, because they felt sorry for her. Helen even took food from other people's plates at meals. Helen's parents took her to see Alexander Graham Bell, the first person to patent the telephone. At one time, Dr. Bell had taught at a school for the deaf. He advised Helen's parents to write to the Perkins Institute for the Blind. The director of the school sent Anne Sullivan, a recent graduate, to teach Helen. Anne first taught Helen the proper way to behave. Then, she began to teach Helen sign language.

Louis attended school. His teacher thought he was a good student, but Louis could only learn by listening. He couldn't read the books the other students read. When Louis was ten, he went to Paris to the National Institute for Blind Children, the world's first school for the blind. At this school, there were books Louis could read. The books had raised letters Louis could touch. The letters were huge, and the books were heavy. Feeling each letter with his fingers took a long time, but at least Louis was reading. Later, Louis was taught sonography, a code of raised dots and dashes. It was invented by a captain in the French army so soldiers could read messages in the dark. Sonography was also known as night writing. The soldiers could read the messages by touching. Louis used sonography to read and write, but it took many dots to write even one word. Louis got an idea. He decided to write his own code. He worked on it late at night when everyone was sleeping and early in the morning before school.

Anne Sullivan used a finger alphabet to teach Helen words. She had Helen hold a doll. Anne spelled d-o-l-l in the palm of Helen's other hand, but Helen did not understand. Anne tried and tried, but Helen didn't understand that the sign language represented letters and words. Then, one day Helen's world changed. Anne and Helen stood at an outdoor water pump. Anne was filling a pail with water. She took Helen's hand and put it under the water and spelled w-a-t-e-r in Helen's other hand. Helen understood that water was the name of what she was feeling. She realized that everything had a name. Helen began touching things such as a tree, a stone, and a fence. She wanted Anne to spell the names of everything.

AMERICAN SIGN LANGUAGE ALPHABET

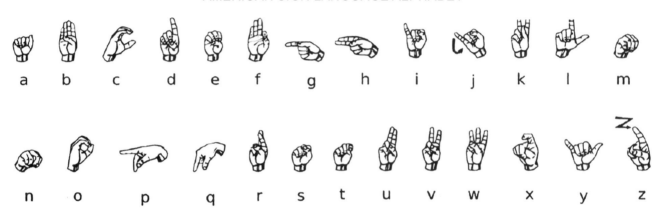

Louis went to the school principal and showed him his system. The new system used raised dots and was a lot easier to learn and read than sonography. At first, Braille's new system was not accepted, but the students at the National Institute recognized how braille was much easier to use than the old system. Many people thought it would be too expensive. Louis and his friend made the first braille writing board. Finally, Louis and other blind people would be able to write. Eventually, Louis Braille became a teacher at the National Institute for the Blind. Louis was a patient, kind, and gentle teacher.

LOUIS BRAILLE'S ORIGINAL FRENCH ALPHABET

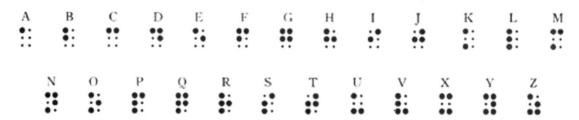

Helen learned thousands of words. Then, Anne Sullivan taught Helen to read using Braille, the raised dot system invented by Louis Braille. Helen also learned to speak. Her speech was hard to understand, because she couldn't hear what she was saying. In 1900, Helen started college. Anne sat next to her and spelled into Helen's hand all that was said. Helen graduated with honors from Radcliffe College. During her college years, Helen wrote *The Story of My Life*. Helen wrote more books and articles about her life and how Anne Sullivan helped her to make sense of the world. Anne died in 1936 after being with Helen for almost fifty years. Helen helped others, especially the blind. During World War II, Helen visited soldiers in hospitals. Meeting Helen gave them hope and encouragement.

Louis Braille and Helen Keller faced many challenges throughout life. Both of them lost their eyesight at a young age. Each of them worked very hard to learn to communicate in spite of their disabilities. Helen and Louis were good students eager to learn. They worked hard to get an education. Both Louis and Helen were fortunate to have excellent teachers in their lives. Through their hard work and determination, Helen Keller and Louis Braille helped many people overcome their disabilities. Even though they died a long time ago, Helen and Louis continue to give hope and guidance to a great number of people.

"In our way, we, the blind, are as indebted to Louis Braille as mankind is to Gutenberg."
                                                                                        - Helen Keller

Note: Johannes Gutenberg changed history with his invention of the printing press. Books did not have to be handwritten. Everyone would have access to books in libraries.

References

Stuckey, Kenneth A. "Keller, Helen". *World Book Online*. www.worldbookonline.com/kids. 28 Feb. 2017.

Stuckey, Kenneth A. "Braille, Louis". *World Book Online*. www.worldbookonline.com/kids. 28 Feb. 2017.

Kent, Deborah. *Helen Keller: Author and Advocate for the Disabled*. The Child's World, 2004.

Freedman, Russell. *Out of the Darkness: The Story Of Louis Braille*. Clarion Books, 1997.

1. Prewriting → Brainstorming

Informative/explanatory writing gives readers information/facts about a topic. The author must research the topic using sources such as books, articles, and the Internet. The author may use illustrations and diagrams to help the reader understand the topic or just to add interest.

An author may not copy information that is found word for word. Notes should be taken when the information is read. The author should make sure he/she understands the information and then change the wording to his/her own words. This is called *paraphrasing*. The sources used should be referenced (cited).

Printed Source Citation

Author Last Name, First Name. Book Title. Publisher, date published.
Freedman, Russell. Out of the Darkness The Story Of Louis Braille. Clarion Books, 1997.

Web Source Citation

Author Last Name, First Name. "Title of Publication". Website Name. URL. Date accessed.
Stuckey, Kenneth A. "Keller, Helen". *World Book Online*. www.worldbookonline.com/kids. 28 Feb. 2017.

Write a informative/explanatory essay about comparing and contrasting two historical figures of interest to you or choose from the writing prompts on page 98.

Brainstorm ideas for a topic for your informative/explanatory essay. Then circle the topic you have chosen.

Which historical figures will be the topic of my informative/explanatory essay?

Write the names of the two historical figures on the line below. Brainstorm how the historical figures are alike and different and write them below your topic.

_____	
Alike	**Different**

1. Prewriting → Planning

Planning is the process of organizing thoughts and ideas for writing.

Use the Venn diagram below to make a plan your informative/explanatory essay. A Venn diagram is a graphic organizer used to compare and contrast two objects, events, people, or concepts. The Venn diagram helps writers understand how two things can be alike and different at the same time.

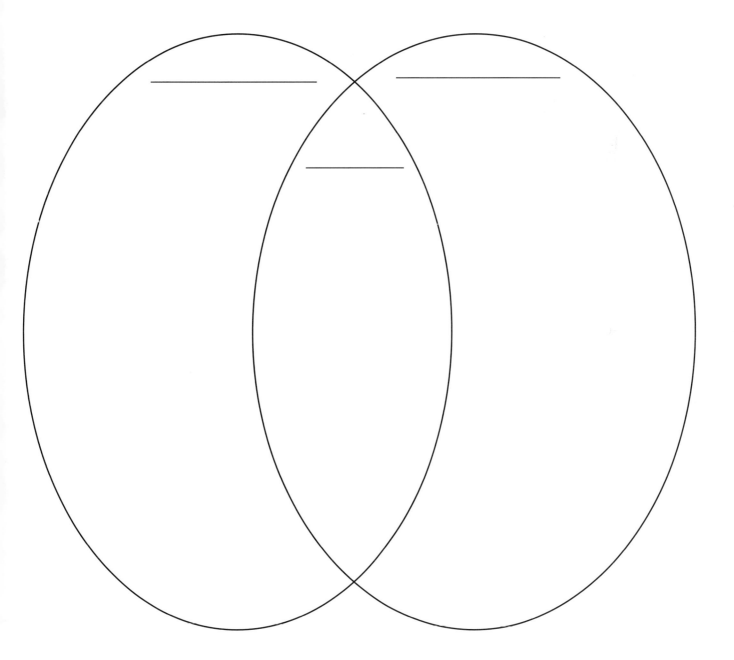

2. First Draft

Use your plans to help you write your first draft.

_____

_____

_____

_____

_____

_____

_____

_____

_____

_____

_____

_____

_____

_____

_____

_____

_____

_____

3. Revising Checklist

Authors revise the text to make their writing better.

Read the first draft of your informative/explanatory essay. Ask yourself the following questions and circle your answers. Use the information you gather from these questions to revise your writing. Write changes on your first draft using arrows (∧) to show where to add words or sentences. Draw a line through words or sentences you've decided to remove.

Niagara Falls
∧
~~It~~ was gigantic.

1. Does my title make the reader want to read my essay?   Yes   No   Maybe

   Notes: _____

   _____

2. Does my first sentence capture the reader's interest?   Yes   No   Maybe

   Notes: _____

   _____

3. Is my essay organized with a beginning, a middle, and an end?   Yes   No   Maybe

   Notes: _____

   _____

4. Did I start a new paragraph for each point?   Yes   No   Maybe

   Notes: _____

   _____

5. Does my essay make sense?   Yes   No   Maybe

   Notes: _____

   _____

6. Did I paraphrase when gathering information?   Yes   No   Maybe

   Notes: _____

   _____

7. Do I need to add more details?   Yes   No   Maybe

   Notes: _____

   _____

8. Do I need to remove any words or sentences?   Yes   No   Maybe

   Notes: _____

   _____

9. Do I have a conclusion paragraph?   Yes   No   Maybe

   Notes: _____

   _____

10. Did I cite sources?   Yes   No   Maybe

   Notes: _____

   _____

Ask a friend or a family member to read your informative/explanatory essay and answer the following questions. Write the answers below the questions.

1. Is there anything you'd like to know more about?

   Notes: _____

   _____

2. Is there anything you don't understand?

   Notes: _____

   _____

3. Revised Draft

Use your notes to revise the first draft of your informative/explanatory essay.

_____

_____

_____

_____

_____

_____

_____

_____

_____

_____

_____

_____

_____

_____

_____

_____

_____

_____

4. Editing Checklist

Reread and edit the revised draft of your informative/explanatory essay. Look carefully for mistakes in spelling, capitalization, punctuation, word usage, and sentence structure.

Spelling

Check for spelling errors. Use a dictionary to help correct spelling errors.

Circle words that are misspelled and write the correct spelling above.

Capitalization

Check to make sure you've capitalized:
- The first word of each sentence
- The word I
- Names of people and pets
- Words like mom, dad, mother, father, aunt, uncle when they are used as names
- Titles when they are used with names
- The first word of a quotation
- Proper nouns–nouns that name a specific person, place, or thing
- Days of week and months of the year

Underline any letters that need to be capitalized.

Punctuation

Check your punctuation: periods, question marks, exclamation points, commas, apostrophes, and quotation marks.

Use an arrow (∧) with the correct punctuation mark above to show where it needs to be inserted.

Word Usage

Read your writing aloud to see if you've used words correctly.

Put a line through words used incorrectly and write the correction above.

Sentence Structure

Check to make sure all of your sentences are complete thoughts. If all of your sentences are simple sentences, try to make some compound or complex.

Put lines through words you do not want to use. Use arrows (∧) to show where words should be added.

5. Publishing

Write the final copy of your informative/explanatory essay with the changes from your editing and revising.

_____

_____

_____

_____

_____

_____

_____

_____

_____

_____

_____

_____

_____

_____

_____

_____

_____

_____

_____

_____

_____

Informative/Explanatory Writing Prompts

1. Think of an invention that you believe is very important to people's lives. After researching the inventor and their invention, tell the story of the invention.

2. Which president would you like to know more about? After researching facts about the president, write about this president and his life.

3. Think of a place in your community you enjoy visiting (museum, zoo, amusement park). Write about this place, and why you think it's a good place to visit.

4. Choose an event in history. Do research to learn more about the event. Write to inform others about this event.

5. Think of a place in nature where you enjoy spending time. Write all about it, include why you like being there.

6. Write about your hometown, including information about size, location, weather, and things to do.

7. Choose a game and explain the directions, the materials, and how to win the game.

8. Explain how to make your favorite sandwich.

9. Choose one of your favorite authors, and write the story of his or her life.

10. Tell step by step how you clean your room.

11. Write a short biography of a member of your family.

12. Interview someone and write about his or her job.

13. Write about how you can conserve water.

14. Write directions telling how to do something.

15. Explain how to earn good grades.

Note: Instead of a Venn Diagram, a different graphic organizer may need to be used for some of these writing prompts.

Informative/Explanatory Writing Rubric

Organization	Voice and Word Choice	Language Arts Standards	Sentence Structure
Score 4 → 90%-100% The writer introduces the topic clearly and captures the reader's interest. The information is written in an organized manner grouping related information together in paragraphs. A strong conclusion restating the main idea in a different way from the introduction is provided.	Score 4 → 90%-100% The writer's voice creates interest and enjoyment for the reader. The writer relates the information clearly and effectively. The writer's personality and feelings are expressed in the writing.	Score 4 → 90%-100% Writing shows a strong command of grade level language arts standards. The writer uses correct capitalization, punctuation, and spelling for the most part.	Score 4 → 90%-100% Sentences are varied: simple, compound, and complex. Sentences are well-developed and are interesting to the reader.
Score 3 → 80%-89% The writer introduces the topic clearly and may capture the reader's interest. The information is written in an organized manner, sometimes separating topics by paragraphs. A conclusion restating the main idea in a different way from the introduction is provided.	Score 3 → 80%-89% The writer's voice creates some interest and enjoyment for the reader. The information is expressed clearly. The writing is lacking a bit in elaboration. Some of the writer's personality and feelings are expressed in the writing.	Score 3 → 80%-89% Writing shows a good command of grade level language arts standards. The few errors in capitalization, punctuation, and spelling do not interfere with understanding.	Score 3 → 80%-89% Sentences are varied for the most part. Sentences are complete and contain details that are interesting to the reader.
Score 2 → 70%-79% The writer introduces the topic. Some of the information is written in an organized manner. A conclusion related to the information presented is provided.	Score 2 → 70%-79% The writer's voice is usually evident. Writing needs more details and organization. Writing shows some feeling. The writer's personality and feelings are vaguely expressed in the writing.	Score 2 → 70%-79% Writing shows some command of grade level language standards. Errors in capitalization, punctuation, and spelling may interfere with understanding.	Score 2 → 70%-79% Sentences are simple with few details. Some sentences are weak or awkward.
Score 1 → Below 70% Writing shows little or no evidence of organization. Very few or no details are given. No conclusion or a weak conclusion is provided.	Score 1 → Below 70% The writer's voice is weak. Few details are provided to interest the reader. The writing is flat. The reader is not engaged.	Score 1 → Below 70% Writing shows little or no command of grade level language standards. Errors in capitalization, punctuation, and spelling interfere with understanding.	Score 1 → Below 70% Sentences are often incomplete or confusing.